FOSSIL

I D E N T I F I E R

FOSSIL
IDENTIFIER

SCOTT WEIDENSAUL

MALLARD
PRESS

MALLARD PRESS

An imprint of BDD Promotional
Book Company, Inc.
666 Fifth Avenue, New York, NY 10103

Mallard Press and its accompanying
design and logo are trademarks of
BDD Promotional Book Company, Inc.

First published in the United States of America
in 1992 by the Mallard Press

ISBN 0-7924-5533-9

This book was designed and produced by
Quintet Publishing Limited
6 Blundell Street
London N7 9BH

Creative Director: Terry Jeavons
Designer: James Lawrence
Project Editor: Lindsay Porter
Editor: Rosemary Booton
Picture Researcher: Scott Weidensaul

Typeset in Great Britain by
Central Southern Typesetters, Eastbourne
Manufactured in Hong Kong by
Regent Publishing Service Limited
Printed in Singapore by Star Standard Industries Pte. Ltd.

Contents

Introduction

Science fiction aside, time travel is not yet possible – unless you gently tap a rock, splitting it along the fractured planes that recall layers of sediment put down long ago. Inside, catching the rays of light for the first time in millions of years, rests the perfect imprint of a trilobite, or the spiralled shell of some long-extinct snail, or the lacy fronds of a primitive fern.

We now know that fossils are the remains of almost unimaginably ancient animals and plants. This knowledge is fairly recent, although

ABOVE *Most ammonites were only a few inches in diameter, but some were substantially larger, like this unidentified, wheel-sized example from England.*

human beings have long been aware of fossils, even if they misinterpreted their origin. To the Chinese, fossils were 'dragon bones', imbued with medicinal value; to Western cultures they were thought to be evidence of the Biblical flood. The first Neandertal skull was dismissed as that of a Cossack soldier or a deformed idiot.

Fossils are intriguing and important on many levels. They allow us to see into our own past, letting us trace our lineage down through the eons – not just our human past, but our prehuman ancestry in reptiles, amphibians, fish and invertebrates, back to the oldest remains of bacterial life, sealed in rock for nearly three and a half billion years. Fossils also hold vital lessons on the fragility of life on this planet, for they underline the constant change wrought by extinction. At the end of the Permian Period, nearly 95 per cent of the living species became extinct – and such catastrophes have occurred not once, but many times. No one who looks at the devastation of species following the mass extinctions of the past can be complacent about the future of human beings.

Knowledge aside, fossils are just plain fun. It is not by accident that fossils are not simply collected; they are hunted by enthusiasts who stalk the richest deposits through detective work and physical labour. The reward comes in the form of a perfect specimen of a long-sought fossil or perhaps in the discovery of a brand-new species. More than in many areas of science, the amateur fossil hunter has an important role to play.

ABOVE *Local museums are an excellent place to learn more about fossils – especially the unusual finds, like this* Eocoelopoma, *an extinct relative of the mackerel.*

BELOW *The trilobite genus* Phacops, *dating from the Silurian and Devonian Periods, is one of the most abundant in North America. This good example came from eastern Pennsylvania.*

What is
a fossil?

We commonly talk about something old as being a 'fossil', but the process requires a lot more than simple age. There must be precisely the right combination of conditions, or else the dead animal or plant will simply decompose into nothing.

LEFT *Still wickedly curved and sharp after nearly 100 million years, this tooth was shed by a sand shark of the genus* Odontaspis. *Teeth fossilize exceptionally well, and in many cases are the only body parts to survive.*

HOW FOSSILS FORM

Under normal circumstances, a dead animal or plant is attacked almost from the time of death by decomposers, ranging from scavenging vertebrates to microbes. Fleshy tissue disappears first, leaving bones, scutes, cartilage, shells and other hard parts. Given time, these, too, vanish.

Very occasionally, however, a carcass, shell or branch settles in a place where oxygen levels are so low that decomposers cannot function. It may be buried in a thick layer of fine mud in a lake delta, swallowed by a landslide or shifting sand dune, or covered over by the constant rain of sediment falling on the ocean floor. The vast majority of fossils are from organisms (including land-dwellers) that finally came to rest in the water.

Because hard parts fossilize more readily than soft tissues, the fossil record is clearest for animals with exoskeletons, bones or shells, and poor for soft organisms and those with thin shells. Happy accidents of geology have pre-

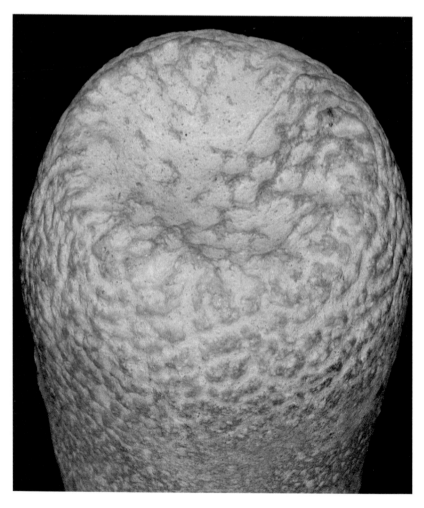

served a few soft-bodied fauna; the justly famous Burgess Shale fossils of western Canada are the best examples, where extraordinarily fine sediment fossilized the most minute details of these invertebrates.

Depending on the original chemical composition of the fossilized piece, its surrounding matrix and the length of time it has been fossilized, the fossil may undergo a chemical change. Petrified wood is a good example: the original cellulose has been replaced by silica, which infiltrated the wood in solution. Sometimes the mineralization only extends to the empty spaces between the wood fibres (permineralization), while in other specimens the wood itself dissolves, to be replaced completely by minerals (replacement). If the wood dissolves, leaving a gap in the harder matrix, and later fills with another mineral, the result is known as a pseudomorph.

These processes can occur not just with wood but with a wide range of fossils. While it is not unusual to find unaltered gastropod

LEFT Having long ago fallen into the ocean, this tree trunk was encased in limestone and eventually dissolved. The mould it left behind was filled with minerals, creating a natural cast, or pseudomorph.

BELOW Primitive, petrified trees dot the landscape in Dorset, England, one of a number of sites worldwide where ancient forests have been uncovered by natural weathering.

OPPOSITE Free of its chalk matrix, a fossilized Siphonia sponge shows the characteristic, budlike shape of the genus. Siphonia lived during the Cretaceous Period.

Permineralization

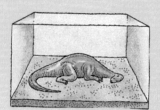

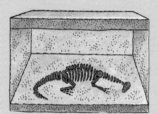

1 The animal dies and falls to the sea or lake bed. The soft parts are decomposed by bacteria, but the hard parts remain.

2 Sediments continually rain down from the water above and settle on and around the skeleton.

3 The sediments compact into rock, and percolating water slowly replaces the chemicals in the bones with hard minerals.

4 Percolating water may dissolve the bones, leaving a mould fossil, or fill the mould with minerals, forming a cast fossil.

ABOVE *Complete replacement of the original organism by a mineral is common – in this case, an ammonoid shell of the genus* Quenstedtoceras *has been replaced by pyrite.*

RIGHT *The minerals that replace the original fossil are almost always harder than the surrounding matrix, which can be removed without damaging the specimen within, as has been done with this* Calymene *trilobite.*

shells that are 150 million years old, many more undergo replacement with such minerals as pyrite or quartz. Plant material (and, more unusually, soft-bodied animals) may undergo carbonization, in which the tissues are converted to a thin carbon film. The beautiful Carboniferous fossils of ferns, horsetails and clubmosses are usually examples of carbonization. If enough vegetation piled up, was buried and compressed, the result is not a thin layer of black, but a seam of coal.

A fossil can take on a number of forms, like the pseudomorph just mentioned. Split open a rock along its bedding plane to reveal a fossil, and you'll often have two matching halves – the fossil itself, known as the part, and its

impression, the counterpart or imprint. Should the specimen dissolve completely, the void it leaves is known as a mould, which preserves the exterior shape of the organism; if the mould fills with another mineral, you have a natural cast, such as a pseudomorph. If the specimen (commonly a gastropod shell) fills with sediment and then dissolves, the resulting fossil is an internal mould, or steinkern. It is not unknown for internal moulds to be found inside external moulds when rocks are split open.

Not everything that appears to be a fossilized organism really is one. Trace fossils are the result of biological activity, but are not the organisms themselves. This category includes faeces (coprolites), burrows, borings, worm tubes, trails and footprints of living things.

While they are not fossils in a strict sense, rock strata may also preserve the effects of

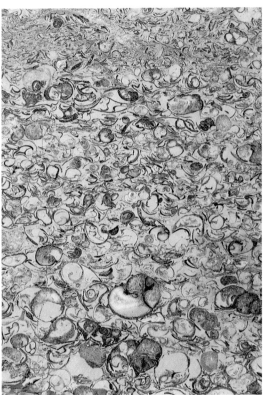

ABOVE *Trace fossils are the evidence of life, but are not the organisms themselves. These internal moulds of segmented worm tracks and tubes were left in the silt of a Cretaceous sea floor and revealed when the rock was split along its bedding planes.*

LEFT *Sliced and polished, this slab of what was once sea bottom is now more fossil shell than rock. Many of the shells (from the Cretaceous gastropod Viviparus elongatus) have been cut into cross-section.*

wind, rain, water currents and other natural phenomena. The most common, perhaps, are the hardened ripples made by water on a muddy lake shore, or desiccation cracks in mud that record a period of drought. Perhaps among the most unusual are tubes of glass, formed in layers of volcanic pumice by lightning strikes; in the broadest of senses, these delicate tubes are 'fossilized' thunderstorms.

THE GEOLOGICAL CALENDAR

The vastness of geological time is hard for anyone to grasp, even an expert used to working with time measured in hundreds of millions of years. One method of putting the scale into perspective is to convert the history of the planet – some 4.5 billion years – into a single calendar year. On such a scale, the most primitive forms of life did not arise until late summer, with protozoans popping up in early autumn, and mankind making an appearance in the waning hours of 31 December.

To break geological time into manageable pieces, palaeontologists use a hierarchical approach, which goes from general to specific through eons, eras, periods and epochs, each unit encompassing shorter stretches of time than the one before. At the moment, therefore, we are in the Phanerozoic Eon, Cenozoic Era, Quaternary Period and Recent (Holocene) Epoch. By way of contrast, the Phanerozoic Eon began about 565 million years ago, while the Holocene Epoch only began 11,000 years ago, or BP (before present).

Unlike days, weeks or months, units of geological time are not of standard length; the Triassic Period lasted about 35 million years, while the Jurassic Period, which followed it, lasted 69 million years. Units of geological time are, after all, arbitrary attempts by people to pigeon-hole history, and the easiest way for palaeontologists to do so is by referring to fossils. In rocks that date to about 65 million years BP, the dinosaurs, which had been the dominant vertebrates for the preceding 130 million years, vanish, to be replaced in younger strata by fossil mammals. This change, known as the Cretaceous-Tertiary (or K-T) Boundary, marks the end of the Cretaceous Period and the beginning of the Tertiary Period. It also forms the boundary between two larger units, the Mesozoic Era and the Cenozoic Era.

These claws are all that remain from a long-dead crayfish of the genus Palaeastacus, *which lived during the Cretaceous period more than 65 million years ago.*

OPPOSITE Lithostrotion *was a highly variable coral from the Upper Palaeozoic, one of the colonial rugose corals that were so plentiful during the Carboniferous Period.*

Mass extinctions form the boundaries of a number of geological time units. The Permian Period of the Palaeozoic Era ended 248 million years BP with the complete extinctions of trilobites, blastoids, eurypterids and several other groups; in addition, there had been great extinctions earlier within the Palaeozoic, at the ends of the Cambrian, Ordovician and Devonian periods.

Opposite is a chronological listing of geological time units in the Phanerozoic Eon, their lengths and the dominant groups in each. The chart begins with the current period, the Holocene, and descends through time. Where boundaries are unclear, a range of dates may be given, and while the sequence is clear, the farther back in time it goes, the less precise the methods for fixing the absolute date.

BELOW *A polished cross-section of* Acervularia, *a Palaeozoic coral, shows radial septae that helped partition the living polyp's body.*

THE GEOLOGICAL CALENDAR

Phanerozoic Eon

600 million years BP – present

Cenozoic Era

63–65 million years BP – present

QUATERNARY PERIOD

Holocene Epoch

11,000 years BP – present

Pleistocene Epoch

1.8–2 million years BP – 11,000 years BP
Climate cooling continues, ice sheets advance; Ice Age megafauna evolve. Mass extinction of megafauna ends epoch. *Homo erectus* appears in early Pleistocene, followed by *Homo sapiens* in late Pleistocene.

TERTIARY PERIOD

Pliocene Epoch

5–7 million years BP – 1.8–2 million years BP
Climate cools, grasslands dominate. First hominids appear early in epoch, followed by australopithecines.

Miocene Epoch

24–26 million years BP – 5–7 million years BP
Mammalian diversity reaches peak. Old World monkeys and apes appear. *Carcharodon*, a huge shark, appears.

Oligocene Epoch

37 million years BP – 24–26 million years BP
Grasses, toothed whales, New World monkeys appear. *Mesohippus* evolves.

Eocene Epoch

54 million years BP – 37 million years BP
First horses (*Eohippus*), elephants, whales, anthropoids.

Palaeocene Epoch

65 million years BP – 54 million years BP
Beginning of the Age of Mammals; first prosimians appear. *Diatryma* and other flightless, predatory birds appear.

Mesozoic Era

225 million years BP – 65 million years BP

CRETACEOUS PERIOD

144 million years BP – 65 million years BP
Flowering plants dominate gymnosperms; dinosaurs include *Tyrannosaurus* and *Triceratops*. Birds, mammals diversifying. Period ends with mass extinction of dinosaurs and ammonoids.

JURASSIC PERIOD

213 million years BP – 144 million years BP
Dinosaurs dominate, including stegosaurs and brontosaurs; *Archaeopteryx*, frogs, salamanders appear. Gondwanaland splits and continents begin to shift towards modern positions.

TRIASSIC PERIOD

248 million years BP – 213 million years BP
Dinosaurs rise to prominence. Ammonoids common in seas; turtles, lizards appear. Pangea splits.

Palaeozoic Era

565 million years BP – 248 million years BP

PERMIAN PERIOD

286 million years BP – 248 million years BP
Reptiles diversify; protomammals and protodinosaurs appear late in period. Mass extinction eliminates trilobites.

CARBONIFEROUS PERIOD

345 million years BP – 286 million years BP
(Including Mississippian and Pennsylvanian periods, also known as Lower and Upper Carboniferous respectively)
Warm, wet climate fosters development of coal-swamp forests. Amphibians dominate on land; ammonoids and brachiopods in sea. Conifers appear.

DEVONIAN PERIOD

395 million years BP – 345 million years BP
Jawless fishes dominate oceans, with trilobites, brachiopods and crinoids. Ammonoids, amphibians, bony fishes appear; first forests.

SILURIAN PERIOD

430 million years BP – 395 million years BP
Fishes diversify; first primitive land plants appear.

ORDOVICIAN PERIOD

500 million years BP – 430 million years BP
Jawless fish appear; wide variety of gastropods, bivalves, brachiopods and other shellfish.

CAMBRIAN PERIOD

565 million years BP – 500 million years BP
Trilobites, shelled invertebrates appear. Nautiloids arise on threshold of Ordovician.

Precambrian Eon

4.6 billion years BP – 565 million years BP
Solar system forms; bacterial life appears 3.5 billion years BP, cyanophytes 3 billion years BP, multicellular life 1 billion years BP.

Collecting Fossils

HOW TO FIND FOSSIL DEPOSITS

Fossils are not distributed randomly through the world's rock strata. Certain kinds of rocks yield abundant fossils, while others are utterly barren, so a basic knowledge of geology will obviously help immensely with your hunting.

Rocks come in three basic varieties – igneous, metamorphic and sedimentary. Igneous rocks are formed from crystallized lava or magma; the best-known examples are granite, obsidian

BELOW While in a state of mild disarray, the bones of this unidentified Devonian fish survived fossilization in excellent shape. The outline of the fleshy parts remains, as does the imprint of entrails, which extruded from the anus after death.

and basalt. Metamorphic rocks are so named because they have undergone fundamental changes due to pressure and heat, from volcanic activity, folding or faulting of strata, mountain-building and other geological activity; shale or clay, for example, may metamorphose into slate, while limestone at high heat and pressure becomes marble.

For obvious reasons, metamorphic and especially igneous rocks are poor hunting grounds for fossils. Instead, you must search

for sedimentary rock, which is created when dust, mud, sand or other soil particles collect in layers, then are solidified (through compaction and other processes) into rock. The same cloudburst that washes a thick new layer of silt into a lake may also carry down the remains of dead animals and plants, which are buried – potential fossils in the making.

Geologists divide sedimentary rocks into clastic rocks, which contain tiny fragments (clasts) of older rock, fossils and minerals, and nonclastic rocks, created by the deposition of minerals or organic material. Sandstone or shale are examples of clastic rocks, while limestone is nonclastic. Clastic rocks are grouped by the

ABOVE *Sea cliffs provide an excellent place to prospect for fossils. This cliff of shale in northern Iceland shows thick beds of several different varieties of fossil bivalves.*

RIGHT *Crinoid ossicles litter this chunk of Carboniferous limestone.*

size of the grains they contain, from the finest-grained argillaceous rocks, through medium-grained arenaceous rocks to the coarsest breccias and conglomerates.

Limestone provides one of the best hunting grounds for fossils, since it was often created from thick deposits of invertebrate shells in the first place. Nummulitic limestone, for example, comes from deposits of foraminiferan tests, while ancient corals were also major contributors to many limestones.

Digging in rocky soil may turn up an occasional lucky find, but for more consistent results you must look for places where the sedimentary bedrock has been exposed, either naturally or, more often, through human activity. They include quarries, road and railway cuts, mines, tunnels and construction sites, as well as natural sites such as outcroppings, fault lines, river banks and coastal or mountain cliffs.

There is no telling where and when a good fossil bed will be uncovered, so develop the

OPPOSITE *At Dinosaur National Monument, specialists work carefully to remove the skeleton of an* Allosaurus, *the one-ton predator of the Jurassic Period. First, the matrix is removed from the upper surfaces of the bones, then a deep channel is carved around them with power tools. Layers of plaster-soaked burlap are applied to the fragile bones to protect them before the entire slab is cut free and taken to the lab, where the skull – with its curved teeth – is freed from the matrix and prepared for display.*

habit of scanning new excavations. Even better, get to know your local excavation contractors and ask them to contact you if they come across anything unusual in the course of their work. Regardless of whether you suspect an area may be worthwhile or receive a tip from someone else, always get permission before prospecting.

Two kinds of sites that can be rich in Ice Age fossils, but which are normally out of reach of amateur collectors, are tar pits and peat bogs – the former because such pits are rare and protected from private collecting, the latter shielded by circumstance, since few beginners can muster the money and manpower needed to excavate a bog. Occasionally, however, bogs yield their treasures unexpectedly, like one in Pennsylvania, USA, that was being mined for peat. The dragline dredged up what the operators thought were chunks of an old stump, but which were discovered to be fragments of a mastodon skull. State palaeontologists walled off part of the bog and excavated the rest of the skeleton from the ooze where the beast had drowned more than 10,000 years before, recovering the most complete mastodon ever found in the United States.

Sometimes, the fossil hunter's work is done by animals. Anthills are the most productive spots to find conodonts, the minute, toothlike fossils from soft-bodied invertebrates, which are carried to the surface by ants in the course of their digging. An examination of anthills may also turn up shark's teeth, bone fragments and tiny mammal teeth.

The best sources of information for the fossil hunter are geological survey departments, which can supply lists of well-known fossil sites open to the public, geological and topographical maps and pertinent regulations. The geology department of a local college or university is another excellent starting place for locating nearby fossil sites, and the faculty may be able to direct you to organizations offering collecting trips. Some departments may even offer enrichment courses for the public that include fossil study.

ABOVE *Much of a fossil's value lies in its relation to the surrounding strata, and the hallmark of a professional dig is meticulous attention to such detail. This sauropod skeleton is being removed very carefully, with each step noted and the position of the bones scrupulously recorded.*

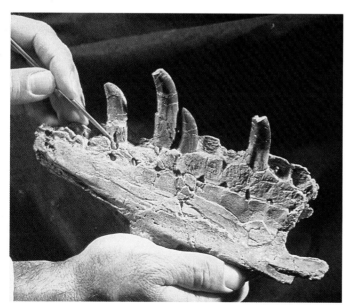

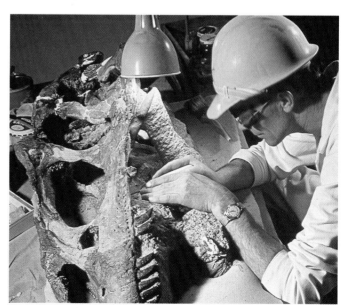

FIELD TECHNIQUES

Anyone can collect fossils with their bare hands, but the good finds aren't always lying on the surface, weathered free in a handy size. For the more serious hunter, a few pieces of equipment are essential. Start with the right clothing: sturdy trousers (knee-pads are a good way to avoid excessive wear and bruised knees), a long-sleeved shirt to prevent sunburn, work gloves, a brimmed hat and heavy boots. Whenever you are working in a quarry, along a high road cut or below cliffs, wear a hard hat, and always wear safety goggles when splitting or hammering rock.

ABOVE *A park ranger explains the skeleton of a baby* Stegosaurus *to visitors in Dinosaur National Monument in Colorado, USA, where tourists can watch palaeontologists excavating dinosaurs from rich Jurassic beds.*

TOP *Not every good specimen weathers free of the matrix in convenient sizes. This fossil fish was brought back to the lab as part of a larger chunk, then trimmed with a rock saw to a neat block for storage.*

Tools and Equipment

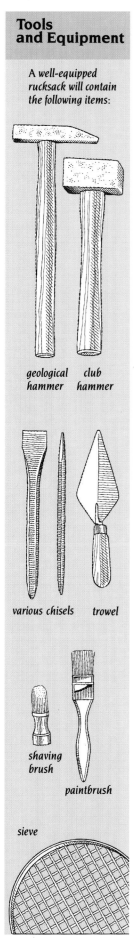

A well-equipped rucksack will contain the following items:

geological hammer   club hammer

various chisels   trowel

shaving brush

paintbrush

sieve

The Fossil Hunter's Workroom

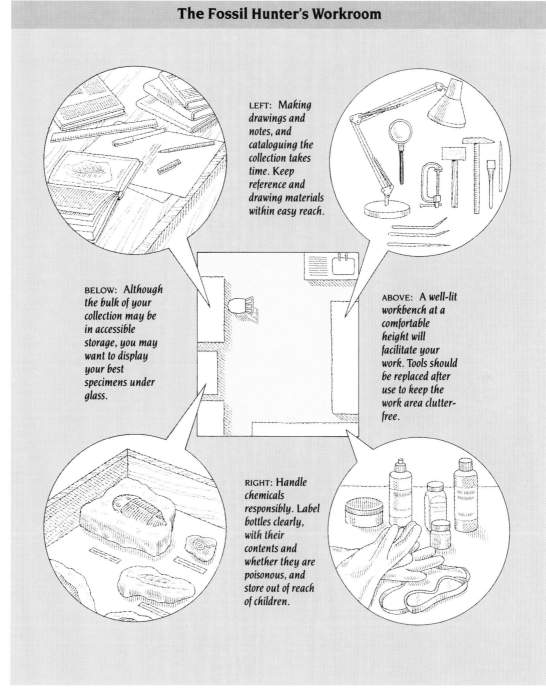

LEFT: *Making drawings and notes, and cataloguing the collection takes time. Keep reference and drawing materials within easy reach.*

BELOW: *Although the bulk of your collection may be in accessible storage, you may want to display your best specimens under glass.*

ABOVE: *A well-lit workbench at a comfortable height will facilitate your work. Tools should be replaced after use to keep the work area clutter-free.*

RIGHT: *Handle chemicals responsibly. Label bottles clearly, with their contents and whether they are poisonous, and store out of reach of children.*

A good knapsack, or the more traditional shoulder bag, should contain a geologist's rock hammer, an assortment of chisels, a good quality hand lens, a small and medium brush (shaving brushes are terrific), a trowel and a sieve; depending on the site and the kinds of fossils you're expecting, a coarse sieve and one with finer mesh may be needed. The knapsack should be big enough for this gear, plus a compass, water bottle, lunch, bags and paper for wrapping specimens.

Your most important pieces of equipment are a notebook and pencil. Good fossil hunters, both professional and amateur, are obsessive note-takers, recording data and making small, detailed sketches of the site, the fossils and their positions in the strata. The importance of good, accurate field notes can hardly be over-stated. If you are a reasonably competent photographer, supplement your field notes with clear photographs, but remember not to fall into the trap of believing that a picture can

Packing and Transporting Fossils

Once the fossil has been excavated, the following should be used for safe transportation:

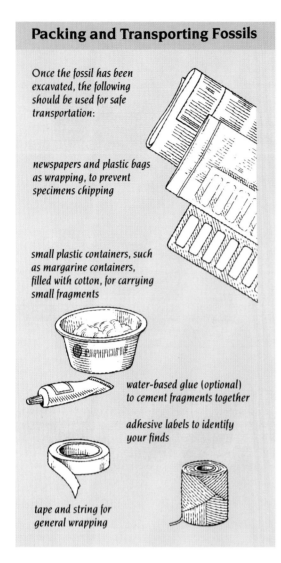

newspapers and plastic bags as wrapping, to prevent specimens chipping

small plastic containers, such as margarine containers, filled with cotton, for carrying small fragments

water-based glue (optional) to cement fragments together

adhesive labels to identify your finds

tape and string for general wrapping

take the place of field notes. A camera does not discriminate, and cannot sort out the important details from the trivial the way the human eye and mind can.

At a minimum, your field notes should record the general and specific location, overall appearance and layout of the exposed bed, with particular attention to the bedding planes

(the surface of old sediment deposits) and their position if they have been inclined through folding. Note the angle of incline (dip) and the strike, which runs at a 90-degree angle to the dip. On your topographical map or a hand-drawn sketch, note compass bearings to several distant points so you can triangulate to find the bed again. The notes should also include descriptions of the rock types and fossils present, both by group and relative abundance, and specific information about the beds and individual positions of the fossils you collect.

Only when the preliminary note-taking is finished should you begin removing fossils. Work with the rock, rather than against it, using the hammer as a last resort rather than an initial attack. Many shales will split apart along bedding planes with hand pressure or a prying twist from an awl or an old knife, for instance, but will fracture from the smack of a hammer. In extraction, less is more – start gently, using the least amount of force necessary, and build gradually until you are successful. Besides being a waste of effort, random hammer blows deface fossil-bearing exposures and destroy fossils.

If you find a worthwhile fossil that is embedded in a piece of matrix too big to collect as it is, you may have to work the fossil free. Allow for a considerable margin of error, as there is nothing more frustrating than cracking a good specimen by trying to trim it too closely. First, experiment on empty rocks of the same type to determine the fragility and splitting characteristics of the rock. Then, using a cold chisel and hammer, chip away at a trough around the fossil, working slowly until the specimen sits atop of a short column of free rock. Finally, aim the chisel at the base of the column and split it – and the fossil – free.

Loose specimens rattling around inside your bag will be chipped and scratched, so wrap each individually in paper, including a temporary label which may be numbered for reference to your field notes. Large plastic bags can be used to segregate wrapped specimens.

CLEANING TECHNIQUES

Many of the specimens will be greatly improved by some judicious cleaning and preparation at home. Because the matrix and the fossil are often of different composition – and thus different hardness – it is usually possible to remove the softer matrix without damaging the fossil. This may be as simple as washing with water and a brush, or may require the use of power tools. Most of the time the effort falls somewhere between these extremes, with the collector patiently removing the matrix with hand tools – small chisels, awls, dental picks and the like – and perhaps trimming the edges to a more presentable appearance with a rock saw. Sometimes the fossil can be removed from a limestone matrix by soaking the specimen in vinegar, which contains acetic acid.

Regardless of what preparation technique you use, always experiment on a worthless specimen from the same site first, just in case something goes wrong, and, when working on the piece containing the fossil, develop the habit of always starting with a hidden surface where unexpected damage won't be disastrous.

BELOW *When selecting fossils for display, choose only your best specimens. This* Fenestella *bryozoan is beautifully preserved, and is sure to impress even a non-collector.*

Spec. # M114   Date: 3/14/90

Species: Echinochama arcinella

Age: Pliocene

Lo   ounty, FL

STORING AND MAINTAINING A COLLECTION

Most collections start out stored in old cigar boxes, but as you develop as a fossil hunter, you will naturally want to take a more professional approach to storing your collection.

There are three basic criteria: the collection must be organized logically; everything must be clearly labelled; and the storage method must not endanger the specimens. Scientific suppliers sell special storage cases for fossils, but anyone handy with wood and tools can make a serviceable cabinet tailored to their needs, available space and budget. The exact style is immaterial, but the case should protect the fossils from direct sunlight and dust, and adjustable partitions in each drawer make it easy to store specimens of many different sizes

and shapes. Alternatively, you may decide to purchase shallow cardboard trays in various sizes. As a final touch, consider installing a glass top above the uppermost drawer, and installing lighting to illuminate your best finds.

Each fossil in your collection needs a pedigree, the paper trail that leads from the field to the display case, without which the specimen is a mere curiosity. Label each specimen by dabbing a spot of white paint on a hidden surface, then writing in the catalogue number in ink. The number corresponds to an entry in your catalogue – traditionally kept in a ledger or a card index, but maintained much more easily today on a home computer, which makes cross-indexing much simpler. The catalogue entry should include identification, age, location and collection date as a bare minimum, and many collectors prefer to give more detailed information.

ABOVE *Home computers make labelling your collection much easier. The specimen number at the upper left refers to a catalogue entry, which includes all pertinent information about the fossils.*

Fossils can easily be misplaced or dropped in the wrong drawer, so don't trust your memory – label each one with a dab of paint and the specimen number written in ink.

BEING A RESPONSIBLE FOSSIL HUNTER

Noble motives do not provide an excuse for ignoble behaviour. Just because fossils are worthless old rocks to many people does not give anyone the right to trespass while collecting them. Always seek permission, and be scrupulous in obeying any requests or rules that the landowner might lay down. (For example, only a portion of a fossil bed may be open, or you may be asked to stay clear of the active areas in a quarry.) Remember that your behaviour may have an impact far beyond your own visit. It doesn't take many bad experiences with thoughtless fossil hunters for a landowner to decide the risks are too high and to close the site completely.

Be considerate of the landowner's property by closing any gates behind you, and staying away from machinery and out of fields. Do not block roads or leave large, unfilled collection pits in your wake. For everyone's peace of mind, get a written letter of permission from the landowner, spelling out where and how you can collect.

Be aware of those who will come after you. Be restrained in your collecting, taking only what you need; while the vast majority of fossils will never be seen by human beings, those few that are exposed in accessible beds are a finite resource, and should be treated with great respect.

Finally, know your limitations. Amateurs have made many important discoveries in the field of palaeontology, but reckless or sloppy extraction, however well-intentioned, may ruin any value the find would otherwise have. If you stumble upon a true rarity, record as much as you can *in situ* and then seek professional help. The discovery will still be yours, and science may be richer for your forbearance.

LEFT *The suture lines in ammonoid shells are important identification clues, but the intricate foldings are beautiful in their own right.*

The Fossils

CYANOPHYTES

CYANOPHYTES IN CHERT

Also known as blue-greens, or blue-green algae, cyanophytes are among the most primitive of organisms, scarcely higher on the evolutionary scale than bacteria. They contain chlorophyll and can photosynthesize like true green plants. Cyanophyte colonies are known as stromatolites, and their distinctive shapes have been found, by microscopic examination, in rocks as old as three billion years. In some tropical lagoons, where evaporating seawater raises the salinity and temperature beyond that which most living things can stand, cyanophytes still make stromatolites, secreting lime to form squat, wide-topped pillars that echo the fossil stromatolites perfectly.

FORAMINIFERANS

Important out of all proportion to their size, these often microscopic protozoans were and are staggeringly plentiful in the oceans, beginning in the Ordovician and continuing through to the present. Their limey tests, falling to the sea floor in thick layers, are a major contributor to the formation of limestone, and are so common that they serve as valuable indicator fossils for palaeontologists, recording past climates.

Camerina spp.

JURASSIC — MIOCENE

One of the larger forams (as this group is commonly called), *Camerina* has a lenticular test that ranges from two-tenths of an inch (0.5 cm) to more than three inches (7.5 cm) in diameter. The test consists of a tightly coiled whorl with thick, calcareous walls and small septae, or chambers. Large and small forms are sometimes divided specifically.

Camerina occured from the Jurassic to the Miocene, but is found in extraordinarily large numbers in deposits from the Eocene, indicating a warm, shallow oceanic environment; beds of *Camerina* limestone have been important since the days of the Ancient Egyptians. It is found in southern Europe, parts of Asia and the South Pacific, and around the Gulf of Mexico.

These forams are still occasionally called *Nummulites*, an obsolete name, and the limestone they formed is known as nummulitic limestone.

NON-FLOWERING PLANTS

Mosses and liverworts were the first land plants but, lacking true roots and a rigid cell structure, they were restricted to extremely moist environments, and grew to only a few inches in height. Later, horsetails, clubmosses and ferns arose with roots and rigid stems, allowing them greater access to the land (although they still required fairly moist soil in which to grow). These are among the most common of fossilized plants, particularly in Carboniferous rocks.

Non-flowering plants reproduce by several methods. Mosses alternate between sterile generations and sexual generations that produce spores; spores are also used by ferns and their relatives. In the more advanced seed-ferns (now extinct), cycads, gingkos and conifers, wind-blown pollen fertilized the cone, which contained eggs and later produced unprotected seeds. Collectively these plants are known as gymnosperms, and while their reproductive system is an improvement on earlier methods, wind-borne pollination is still quite chancy.

A number of genera in this group, such as *Stigmaria* and *Calamites*, have since been shown to belong to several different families; *Stigmaria*, for instance, are the fossilized roots of a variety of species of clubmosses of the genus *Lepidodendron*.

Calamites

CARBONIFEROUS

Horsetails were an important part of the Carboniferous forests; this species, one of the more common fossils from this period, reached heights of 60 feet (18 m). The fossils represent stems, which were longitudinally ridged and in jointed segments of varying lengths, depending on the specimen.

Only recently was it discovered that *Calamites* is the trunk of the same plant whose leaves were known as *Annularia*. The names have been retained to avoid confusion.

Horsetails remain common wetland plants in many parts of the world, but the surviving species are small, usually no more than waist-high. The stems are stiffened with cellular silica, which gives them a rough texture that lends itself to scrubbing cooking pots – hence the American pioneer name 'scouring rush'.

Annularia

CARBONIFEROUS

The whorled, slightly spatulate leaves of *Annularia* are common in Pennsylvanian deposits; they are the leaves of the same sphenophyte horsetail whose stems were once mistakenly assigned to the genus *Calamites*. In the specimen shown, the leaf clusters have been dislodged and have fossilized individually, but they are frequently found still attached to the upper surface of the twig, which apparently grew out of the joint-nodes of the *Calamites* stem.

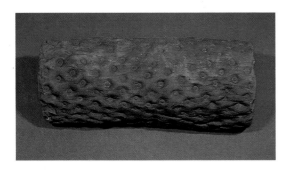

Stigmaria ficoides

CARBONIFEROUS

Not a true genus unto itself, *Stigmaria* are the fossilized roots of tree clubmosses, *Lepidodendron*; while not a strictly correct usage, *Stigmaria* has been retained for simplicity's sake. Lycopods such as *Lepidodendron* are common fossils from the Carboniferous, and apparently formed a significant portion of the coal-swamp forests. While most surviving clubmosses are small, this genus attained heights of more than 150 feet (46 m), with a heavily scaled trunk and wide-spreading root system. The genus is extinct, but at its peak numbered more than 100 species, judging from the fossil record.

Stigmarid roots are usually found as casts, in sediment layers immediately beneath coal seams – layers that once were the soil in which the clubmoss trees grew.

Pecopteris spp.

CARBONIFEROUS

Pecopteris was a true fern, or pteridophyte, although there is a suspicion that some members of the genus had developed into seed-ferns, a trait difficult to determine from car-

bonized fossils. True ferns represented several 'firsts' in evolutionary history, including the first complex leaves and branched stems. These features, coupled with an improved vascular system, allowed the true ferns to evolve quickly into giants nearly 50 feet (15 m) tall. Ferns today are much smaller, inhabiting the shade of the more advanced angiosperm trees, which now dominate the world's forests.

Alethopteris spp.

CARBONIFEROUS

The coal-swamp forests of the Carboniferous covered a great deal of what is now the Northern Hemisphere, so that many of the distinctive plant fossils of that period can be found in the United States, Europe and Asia. *Alethopteris* is a seed-fern (pteridosperm) that is common in this stratum; it has relatively thin, tapered leaflets that are straighter than many of its close relatives.

Seed-ferns were a big step forward in plant evolution. By enclosing the plant embryo in a tough, resilient cover and supplying it with nourishment, the seeds would not have to find perfect growing conditions immediately, but could hold out for longer periods of time, germinating when the environmental situation improved.

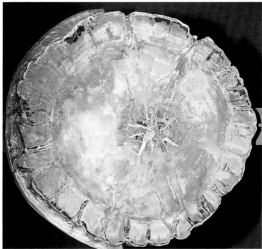

Petrified wood

TRIASSIC

Petrified wood is an unusual fossil with a wide distribution; there are significant sites in North America and Europe, as well as elsewhere. This specimen comes from the famous Petrified Forest National Park in Arizona, where primitive protopines, *Araucarioxylon*, were buried in saturated sediment and replaced with agate and jasper, creating a kaleidoscope of colours in each example.

While true petrified wood may preserve even the cellular structure, many more trees have been fossilized as moulds or pseudomorphs, which record only the external structure of the log or root system, with none of the internal detail.

Glossopteris

TRIASSIC

Glossopteris is a critically important fossil in determining the make-up of the prehistoric supercontinent known as Gondwanaland. It has been found in most of the southern land-masses that once made up Gondwanaland, including Antarctica, which had a subtropical climate at the time. Most fossils are of single leaves, lanceolate or spatulate. *Glossopteris* was a pteridosperm that grew into tree form, first appearing during the Permian and remaining common through the Triassic, when this specimen from New South Wales was fossilized.

ABOVE *Amber.*

Amber

Many trees, particularly conifers, secrete a gummy resin when injured. The resin seals the wound against insects, disease and desiccation, and under some conditions it may harden into a honey-coloured globule of amber.

Amber was apparently prized by Palaeolithic man, and by the time of the Ancient Celts it was an important jewellery item, but its value to palaeontologists is less aesthetic and more practical. Insects and arachnids often become mired in tree resin, and those trapped in amber display an astounding degree of preservation, even though they are actually hollow moulds with thin, carbonized layers around the outside. This is especially fortunate because insects rarely fossilize otherwise, so much of our knowledge of prehistoric insects comes from amber specimens.

FLOWERING PLANTS

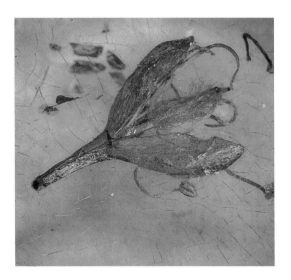

Hymenaea spp.

AGE UNKNOWN

First appearing in the fossil record roughly 100 million years BP, flowers represented a major advance in plant reproduction. By bribing insects (as well as other animals such as birds and bats), the plants enjoyed a much higher rate of pollination success, while greatly reducing their biological investment. Instead of dumping vast quantities of pollen into the wind, the flowers produce sweet nectar to lure the animal, which is dusted with pollen from the stamens while eating. When the animal visits the next flower of the same species, the pollen is brushed against the female stigmas, and reproduction occurs.

The earliest angiosperms, or flowering plants, were the magnolias, which arose during the Cretaceous. Shown here is a flower from a species of *Hymenaea*, a member of the vast legume family.

INVERTEBRATES

The term 'invertebrates' loosely describes those animals above the protist level that do not possess backbones. Including such well-known fossils as brachiopods, molluscs and trilobites, they are by far the most commonly found examples of prehistoric life, and make up the bulk of most fossil collections.

SPONGES (PHYLUM PORIFERA)

Simplistic in design, sponges are simply aggregations of cells: in fact, there remains uncertainty as to whether sponges are individual animals or colonies of single-celled animals. Form is provided by spicules – minute rods that may fuse to form a skeleton for the sponge – or sponges may exist in unfused form. Some, like *Siphonia*, have siliceous spicules, while others, such as *Raphidonema*, possess calcareous spicules. Still others gain rigidity from a material called spongin, and lack spicules. The fossil record for sponges is patchy, but begins in the Precambrian.

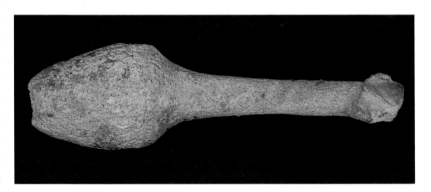

Siphonia spp.

CRETACEOUS

Flower-shaped, the stalked sponges of the genus *Siphonia* had siliceous spicules, a large central cavity in the budlike body, and a network of tiny openings that connected to a primitive vascular system. *Siphonia* were 'rooted' at the end of the stalk to the sea bed, and like all sponges depended on the ocean currents to bring them food particles.

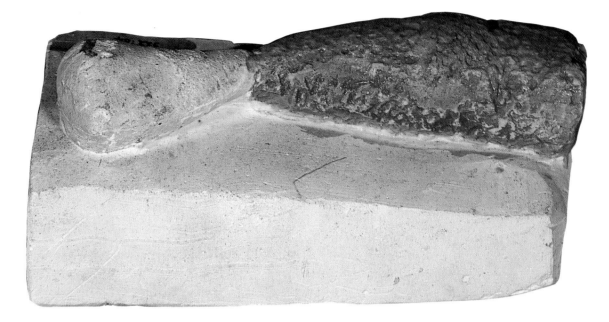

Ventriculites spp.

CRETACEOUS

Species of the genus *Ventriculites* show a distinctive, vase-shaped body with a fused spicule construction; the body walls are thin and have large pores. This genus belongs to the group of sponges known as lychniskids, which have a unique spicule construction in which diagonal braces buttress the form, creating a pattern that is reminiscent of a Greek lantern, on which the group name is based.

The species shown is V. *longitudinalis*. Like *Siphonia*, *Ventriculites* is a strictly European genus, and while it was common during the Cretaceous, it is rare in today's oceans.

Raphidonema spp.

CRETACEOUS

Unlike the preceding two sponge genera, the sponges of the genus *Raphidonema* have calcareous spicules, rather than siliceous; the spicules have three limbs, and are fused into a rigid skeleton. The overall appearance of the sponge is that of an open, widely flared vase, often heavily folded and covered with large pores and lumps. The length is usually two inches (5 cm) or less. The species shown is R. *parcatum*.

ABOVE Ventriculites longitudinalis.

RIGHT Raphidonema parcatum.

CORALS, JELLYFISH AND HYDROZOANS (PHYLUM CNIDARIA)

This phylum includes aquatic, radially symmetrical animals. Unlike sponges, they have definite tissue layers, but remain very simple organisms, lacking internal organs and a central nervous system. There are two major body plans – the polyp, a sedentary, columnar form often with tentacles around the oral opening, and the medusa, a flattened, free-swimming variation of the polyp. Both are radially symmetrical around an axis that runs through the central oral opening. Anemones, corals and hydra are examples of polyps, while jellyfish are medusae, although in many living genera, generations alternate between the two forms.

The class Anthoza includes many colonial species with hard, calcareous skeletons, which fossilize exceptionally well. The corals belong to this class, which arose during the Ordovician.

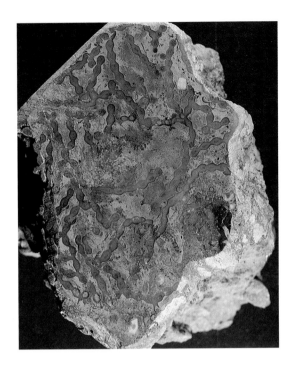

Halysites spp.

SILURIAN

Often known as chain coral, Halysites is one of the tabulate corals, a group of colonial cnidarians; the specimen shown, H. cantenularius, has been cut in cross-section, revealing the individual corallites with their tabulae, the horizontal sections that give this group its name. In life a Halysites colony would have been a series of long, thin, upright tubes, joined along the edges. Adjoining walls in tabulate corals were sometimes pierced by a series of holes called mural pores, but these are not found in Halysites.

Favosites

SILURIAN—DEVONIAN

One of the most common fossil corals of the middle Palaeozoic, Favosites is a tabulate coral with irregularly five-sided corallites, in cross-section. The walls of the corallite, which was

secreted by the coral animal, are thin and pocked with mural pores, while the tabulae are closely packed. The corallum may be large and irregularly shaped. Because of its shape, Favosites is often known as honeycomb coral.

Tabulate corals were common reef-builders in the middle and upper Palaeozoic, providing the foundation of the reef, and the living space for many other species of marine invertebrates. Even more so than other corals, tabulate corals seemed to change growth patterns as environmental conditions altered, making identification difficult at times.

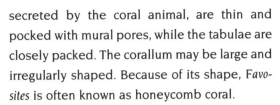

Zaphrentis

DEVONIAN—MISSISSIPPIAN

One of the Rugose, or horn, corals, Zaphrentis was a solitary species that secreted a cup-shaped corallite; the inside of the 'cup' is lined with ridge-like septae, which are the vertical interior walls of the corallite. The pointed end of the coral would have originally been anchored in mud, with the open end of the cup facing upwards so the coral animal could filter food particles from the water.

Acervularia spp.

SILURIAN—DEVONIAN

One of the colonial rugose corals, Acervularia form large, usually four-sided corallites with pronounced septae. A. ananus, shown here, is found in European sediments.

The rugose corals had six major septae, which in life would have provided support for six corresponding menesteries, bands of tissue that divided the coral polyp's body. The rugose corals reached their zenith in the Silurian and Devonian, and disappeared by the Lower Mesozoic.

Paleosmilia spp.

CARBONIFEROUS

One of the rugose corals, *Paleosmilia* is found in both haploid (solitary) and compound (colonial) forms. The hallmark of this genus is the tightly packed septae; in *Paleosmilia* the septae are radially symmetrical, rather than bilaterally symmetrical, as are most other rugose corals.

Lithostrotion spp. (Acrocyathus)

DEVONIAN — MISSISSIPPIAN

A highly variable coral, *Lithostrotion* corallites may be pentagonal, round or four-sided, but are always marked by cone-shaped tabulae and a conical lump in the centre of the calice, or cup, ridged by septae; the corallites are often long and sinuous. This genus was a colonial rugose coral, with colonies growing to widths of more than 12 inches (30 cm) and forming a significant portion of the fossil reefs of the Carboniferous.

Lithostrotion fossils are found in widely scattered parts of the globe, including most of the Northern Hemisphere, Africa and Australia.

Scleractinid corals

TRIASSIC — RECENT

The scleractinids include the sea anemones and the stony corals, the latter being far more important to the fossil record than the soft, rarely fossilized anemones. Scleractinids – or hexacorals, as they are sometimes known – may be solitary or colonial, and include all the world's living hard corals. Shown is an unidentified species of scleractinid from the Jurassic.

BRYOZOANS (PHYLUM BRYOZOA)

Similar at first glance to corals or plants (leading to the vernacular name 'moss animals'), bryozoan colonies are common fossils from the Ordovician onward. Each individual animal is a polyp-like zooecia, which secretes an exoskeleton, often calcareous. Fossil colonies often show a branching form marked with small openings known as zooids.

Bryozoans remain common marine animals. Adults 'brood' the young in special compartments, releasing the larvae into the water when their development is complete. The larvae pass through a planktonic phase before settling down to form a new colony. They do so by attaching themselves to a surface, then 'degenerating' into a small mass of larval tissue, from which new individuals, known as ancestrulae, grow. Each ancestrula then produces buds, which in turn bud themselves, expanding the colony. As it grows, the shape and function of the colony may change to adapt to changing environmental conditions.

As the photograph below of bryozoan fragments shows, the shape of fossil bryozoans is varied, from flattened funnels like *Fenestella* (see below), to crusting coverings, to delicate branches. These fragments date from the Miocene, and were found in New Zealand.

ABOVE Fenestella *sp.*

BELOW *Bryozoan fragments.*

Fenestella spp.

ORDOVICIAN—PERMIAN

This common lace bryozoan formed colonies that fanned out gracefully, with thin cross-bars linking the branches. Each branch possessed twin rows of zooids, on one side only, so that a pseudomorph of the wrong side of a *Fenestella* colony may not show the zooids. The species shown is F. *plebeia* from the Mississippian.

BRACHIOPODS (PHYLUM BRACHIOPODA)

Superficially resembling bivalves, brachiopods are shellfish with valves (shells) of unequal size, and are the largest and most important group of fossil animals. Extremely common in sediments from shallow oceans, brachiopods first appear in the fossil record during the Lower Cambrian, and although a few hundred species survive, they reached their zenith during the Devonian.

There are two classes: the Inarticulata and the Articulata, separated by the lack of a hinge between the two valves in the Inarticulata. Living forms are known as lampshells, because of the resemblance of the lower (or pedicle) valve to a Roman oil lamp. Brachiopods are usually permanently fixed to the substrata by a fleshy stalk that protrudes from a hole in the pedicle valve, known as the pedicle foramen. As a general rule, the larger of the two valves was the ventral valve in life.

Brachiopods, typical of shellfish, are filter-feeders. The feeding organ, known as the lophophore, is covered with fine, hairlike cilia that beat in sequence, creating a current that draws food-bearing water into the shell, where tiny organic particles are strained out before the water is expelled. The branches of the lophophore are known as brachia, and are supported by calcified brachidium, which form complex spirals in some brachiopods.

RIGHT Sphaeroidothyris sphaeroidothyris.

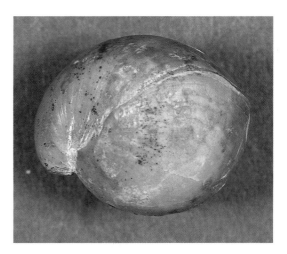

LEFT Obovothyris magnobovata.

Obovothyris magnobovata

JURASSIC

Bulbous in shape, *Obovothyris* is a ribless brachiopod with a small pedicle foramen and a strongly curved umbo, the 'point' or beak of the pedicle valve. Length is usually half an inch (1.5 cm) or less. The species illustrated is O. *magnobovata* from the Jurassic, a fossil found today in Europe.

Sphaeroidothyris sphaeroidothyris

JURASSIC

Similar to *Obovothyris*, *Sphaeroidothyris* is another bulbous Jurassic brachiopod with poorly defined growth lines on the valves.

Rhynchonellida brachiopods

ORDOVICIAN–RECENT

A large group of articulated brachiopods, rhynchonellids have a well-developed pedicle foramen wedged between a pair of deltidial plates on the umbo. Most species have strong, radial ribbing, with a simplistic internal support for the lophophore, Surviving rhynchonellids differ little from those fossilized more than 500 million years BP; most lived (and still live) on muddy sea bottoms.

The genus name *Rhynchonella* is used (primarily in Europe) as an umbrella term for dozens of species of rhynchonellids, which are sometimes so abundant in deposits that they form coquina, a rock made up solely of fossilized shellfish. The specimen illustrated is R. *capex* from the Silurian, showing the brachial valve.

BELOW Rhynchonellida capex.

Lobothyris punctata

JURASSIC

Lobothyris is one of the terebratulid brachiopods, which have strongly biconvex shells, well-developed umbones and pedicle foramen; in this genus, the valves are smooth except for distinct, concentric growth marks. *Lobothyris* apparently mastered a difficult environment that other brachiopods could not tolerate, and it is found in great numbers, either by itself or with one other genus, *Tetrarhynchia*, a small, ribbed, triangular brachiopod. In the absence of competition, they dominated their particular niche, which today has been transformed into ironstone deposits.

Gibbithyris spp.

CRETACEOUS

Globular and smooth, this small brachiopod has biconvex valves and a very small pedicle foramen. Growth lines are obvious and closely spaced on *Gibbithyris*, a common fossil from England. It belongs to a group of brachiopods known as terebratulids, which feature strong umbones and hinge lines less than the width of the valves at their widest point. Most of the surviving brachiopods are terebratulids.

Rugitela spp.

JURASSIC

Rugitela has distinct growth lines on its valves, which reach a maximum of 1½ inches (4 cm) in large specimens. The foramen is small and the umbo long and sharply hooked, curving back on the brachial valve.

Plectothyris spp.

JURASSIC

A small brachiopod, *Plectothyris* has biconvex valves and a well-developed umbo pierced by the pedicle foramen. The valves are ribbed, especially along the anterior edges. The tip of the umbo has been cracked off in this specimen, revealing plain rock – for this, like many fossils, is a natural cast, retaining only the external shape of the animal that made the mould before dissolving away.

ABOVE Leptaena rhomboidalis

Leptaena spp.

ORDOVICIAN – SILURIAN

This genus of articulate brachiopods has a distinctive shape – the brachial valve is concave, while the pedicle valve is convex, and the anteriors of the valves meet at right angles, forming a squared-off front. It is finely ribbed, with coarse, concentric rings. Palaeontologists theorize *Leptaena* lived partially buried in the ocean. The specimen shown is L. *rhomboidalis* for the famous Wenlock limestone deposits in England.

MOLLUSCS (PHYLUM MOLLUSCA)

A diverse phylum, the *Mollusca* include three broad classes – the gastropods (snails and slugs), bivalves (clams and their relatives) and cephalopods (octopi, squid, nautiloids and ammonoids) – and three smaller classes, the *Monoplacophra*, *Scaphopoda* (tusk-shells) and the *Polyplacophora* (chitons). Their shells fossilize readily, making them among the most important of all fossil phyla.

CLASS **GASTROPODA**

Gastropods are univalves, with single, coiled, unchambered shells (although some genera have no shells at all, and a few have straight, uncoiled shells). They are the most common molluscs in the fossil record.

It is not always clear to a neophyte (either fossil hunter or beachcomber) how a gastropod moves, since only the shell is left after death. What is missing from the fossil or the wave-tossed shell is the soft animal, with its large, muscular foot that allows the gastropod to glide along the bottom. The foot and head can be withdrawn into the aperture in the event of danger, and the opening sealed with a horny plate known as the operculum.

The shell of a gastropod hides the paired gills, feathery organs in the rear of the body whorl. Water is pumped into the shell, circulated around the gills, then expelled.

Turritella spp.

CRETACEOUS—RECENT

A long, tapered spire with slightly flattened or gently convex whorls distinguishes *Turritella*, a common fossil in strata laid down in shallow oceans. Depending on the species, the shell is usually two inches (5 cm) or less in length with the whorls ribbed or keeled, and the aperture (or shell opening) varying from rounded to square. Known as turret shells, *Turritella* remains a common gastropod in warm oceans, and the fossils are found almost worldwide in appropriate Tertiary deposits, making it an important index species.

ABOVE Turritella *sp.*

ABOVE RIGHT
Neptuna contraria.

LEFT Viviparus
sussexiensis.

BELOW Scaphella
lamberti.

Viviparus spp.

CRETACEOUS—RECENT

Viviparus snails had smooth, generously rounded whorls and moderate spires, with large, circular apertures. The photograph shows specimens of the species V. *sussexiensis* from Europe. A surviving member of the genus, V. *georgianus*, the Georgia apple snail, is a common freshwater species in the southern United States; it, presumably like its fossilized ancestors, gives birth to live young.

Neptunea spp.

CRETACEOUS—RECENT

Still an abundant genus in the world's oceans, *Neptunea* whelks first appear in the fossil record in the Cretaceous; the photograph shows N. *contraria* of the Pleistocene alongside its modern equivalent, the smooth whelk, while another living relative, the ten-ridged whelk, inhabits subtidal waters of the North Atlantic. *Neptunea* shells have large, smooth body whorls and moderately tapered spires; the aperture is oval, forming a teardrop where it meets the siphonal canal.

Scaphella spp.

CRETACEOUS—RECENT

Living *Scaphella*, known as volutes, are colourfully marked shells popular with collectors in warm-water areas. Fossils of this genus usually have nodes on the whorls, and four folds on the columella, the central pillar of the shell that surrounds the imaginary axis around which the gastropod coils. The species shown is S. *lamberti* from the Pleistocene.

In most gastropods, the earliest shell growth – the protoconch – is recorded at the very apex of the shell as a tiny, calcareous whorl. In *Scaphella*, however, the first secretions are horny and temporary, dropping off after the calcareous shell is secreted, and leaving a small point as evidence of their presence.

Athleta spp.

ABOVE Athleta lucator.

RIGHT Conus *sp.*

CRETACEOUS—RECENT

A robust fossil whelk, Athleta (formerly *Voluta*) has weak to strong nodes which may form short spines, and a long, slightly curved siphonal canal. The body whorl is ribbed. This genus includes a wide variety of living species, while fossil forms were especially important during the Cretaceous and Tertiary. The species shown is A. *luctator* from the Eocene.

LEFT Clavilithes macrospira.

Clavilithes spp.

CENOZOIC

This genus features a relatively long to moderate spire, shouldered whorls and faint longitudinal ridging on the whorls. The long siphonal canal is missing from this specimen of C. *macrospira* from the Eocene.

The protoconch on *Clavilithes* is a form known as mammillated, since it takes the shape of two squat, rounded whorls, which are unornamented. In gastropods, the remainder of the shell is called the teleoconch.

Conus spp.

CRETACEOUS—RECENT

So widespread that they serve as index fossils for the Cenozoic, *Conus* shells have flat to short spires with small, tightly wound apicle whorls and a large body whorl with a long, narrow aperture slit at each end. The whorls are usually smooth except for growth lines.

Conus remains one of the most diverse genera of gastropods, with about 350 living species, most found in warm, shallow inshore waters. They are active predators, harpooning other molluscs, worms and fish with a specialized 'tooth' and subduing their prey with venom. The venom of some Indo-Pacific species, like the textile cone, has caused human deaths.

Aptyxiella spp.

JURASSIC—CRETACEOUS

One of the most graceful of Jurassic fossils, *Aptyxiella* has a long spire, which in some species becomes extremely tapered, stretching several inches in length, with a tiny aperture and slight indentations on the insides of the whorls.

The specimens shown, of A. *portlandica*, are natural casts, formed when sediment entered the shell; the shells later dissolved, leaving a replica of their interiors.

Pleurotomaria spp.

JURASSIC—CRETACEOUS

The shell of *Pleurotomaria* forms a broad cone, with slight knobbing on the shoulders and growth lines on the whorls that give the appearance of ridging; the aperture is rounded, with a pronounced slit in the outer lip. *Pleurotomaria* is a common gastropod fossil in many Upper Mesozoic deposits worldwide. The specimen shown is P. *bitorquata*.

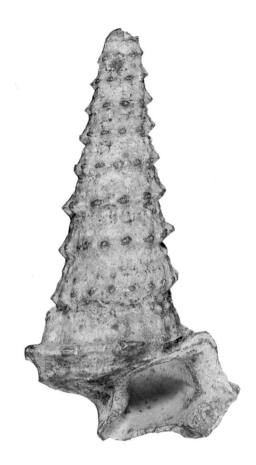

Cerithium spp.

CRETACEOUS—RECENT

A small shell, *Cerithium* has a long spire with a sharp apical angle, aperture lips that may flare, and a short, curved siphonal canal; the whorls may be knobbed or ridged with growth lines, or flat and almost unornamented. Modern species, known as ceriths, are highly ornamented and colourful, and inhabit ocean shallows and reefs. Shown is C. *duplex* from Europe.

CLASS BIVALVIA

Easily confused by beginners with brachiopods, bivalves also have two shells, but the valves are virtual mirror images of each other, since the plane of symmetry is horizontal in bivalves, rather than vertical as in brachiopods. The shapes may be subtriangular, triangular, ovoid or circular.

Many bivalves are adapted for burrowing, using the long, muscular foot to pull themselves through the mud or sand, while others glue themselves permanently to one spot, and still others (like scallops) clap their valves violently and 'swim' awkwardly through the water.

Anthracosia and Carbonicola spp.

CARBONIFEROUS

Two of the most interesting fossil bivalves, these two small species were strictly freshwater inhabitants, living in the coal-swamp forests and marshes of the Carboniferous – among the first bivalves to make the change from saltwater to fresh. The *Carbonicola* shell is subtriangular, with a curved hinge line and minor growth-line ridging. A*nthracosia* belongs to the same family, and is essentially similar. In some areas, deposits of these two shells (sometimes mixed with a third, N*aiadites*) form 'mussel beds' that may be six feet (2 m) or more thick. Shown are the species A, *atra* (left) and C. *communis*.

Cardium spp.

TRIASSIC — RECENT

One of the bivalves popularly known as cockles, *Cardium* has valves that appear heart-shaped in profile, with pronounced ribbing (costae) on the external surfaces and distinct muscle scars

on the interior. The species illustrated is C. *parkinsoni* from the Pleistocene. The *Cardium* are heterodonts, meaning that they possess lateral teeth on the hinge, in addition to the central radiant, or cardinal, teeth.

Contrary to expectations, the front and rear of a bivalve are the 'sides' as the shell is held flat in the palm of the hand; as a rule of thumb, the beak points towards the anterior, or front. As mentioned, *Cardium*, like many fossil bivalves, retains the roughened patches where the adductor muscles, which hold the shell closed, were attached to the inside of the valve.

Gryphaea spp.

TRIASSIC — JURASSIC

The odd shell construction of this genus, in which one valve is considerably larger than the other, resulting in a snail-like curl, is known as an inequivalve; the left is by far the larger of the two, with a curved umbo (especially pro-nounced in the species illustrated, G. *arcuata*), while the right valve is small and flat or concave. Heavy growth lines form concentric ribbing on the valves. The animal was sedentary, living affixed by its left valve to the ocean floor.

Myphorella spp.

JURASSIC — CRETACEOUS

The distinguishing feature of this Upper Mesozoic bivalve is the concentric rows of knobs, sometimes growing out of costae, that cover the triangular to subtriangular valves, with a sharp beak at the dorsal margin. The species shown is M. *hudlestoni*; these bivalves are sometimes assigned to the genus *Trigonia*, and apparently were burrowing shellfish.

Pleuromya spp.

TRIASSIC — CRETACEOUS

By comparing fossil species with living forms (whose lifestyles are known), palaeontologists try to deduce how extinct animals lived. Because *Pleuromya* is a desmodont bivalve, with no true hinge teeth, it is believed that it was a burrower, since a buried bivalve has little need for an efficient open-and-close mechanism in the shell. Some heterodonts also burrow, and the fossil record traces the loss of their hinge teeth as well.

Pleuromya is an equivalve bivalve, oval to trapezoidal in shape. External ornamentation may include concentric ribbing, which is more pronounced in some specimens than others.

Glycymeris spp.

CRETACEOUS — RECENT

A common genus in the world's oceans, *Glycymeris* is also abundant in the fossil record from the Cretaceous on. Most species are circular to slightly oval, equivalve, with large umbones; external ornamentation comprises costae, varying in development, and growth lines. Shown is G. *deleta* from the Eocene, and a mass of unidentified *Glycymeris* fossils, also from the Eocene.

RIGHT Neithea
sexcostata.

Neithea spp.

CRETACEOUS

Found abundantly worldwide in Cretaceous
deposits, Neithea is a lovely inequivalve genus,
with its right valve far more convex than the
left, which is flattened. The ribbing pattern is
distinctive and attractive, with four to six large,
roughly equal ribs separated by three or four
smaller ribs, creating a scalloped pattern along
the anterior margin. The species shown is N.
sexcostata.

RIGHT Venericardia
planicosta.

Arctica spp.

CRETACEOUS—RECENT

As the genus name suggests, clams of the
genus Arctica showed a preference for cold
waters, making them valuable as environmental indicators. The valves are typical of cold-
water clams – oval to circular, with curved
umbones and no external ornamentation beyond the growth lines. Shown above are A.
planata, a fossil from the Eocene, and a Pliocene
specimen of the species A. islandica. The latter
is a living species, known as the black clam,
and appears commonly as a beach shell on
North Atlantic shores.

BELOW Venericardia
senilis.

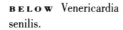

Venericardia spp.

CRETACEOUS/PALAEOCENE—
EOCENE

Large cockles with heavy, triangular valves,
low, flat costae and concentric growth lines,
Venericardia have two large, curved hinge teeth.
There are a number of living, cold-water species,
found from the lower intertidal zone to several
hundred feet of water. The fossil specimens
shown are V. planicosta from the Eocene and V.
senilis from the Pliocene. Members of this genus
have at times been assigned to Cardita and
Cyclocardia.

Plicatula spp.

JURASSIC—RECENT

Plicatula is a typical isodont, a bivalve with two identical teeth and two sockets in each valve, placed symmetrically. Illustrated is a Jurassic species, P. *spinosa*. Other specimens from the Jurassic have been found still retaining their natural colour, and are among the few examples of coloured shells being found as fossils. One of the living members of *Plicatula*, the kitten's paw (P. *gibbosa*), is popular with shell collectors along Florida's Gulf coast, and some fossil species greatly resemble its shape, which actually does look like a flattened cat's paw.

Plicatula cements itself in place, thus securing a permanent foothold – a necessity, since this genus prefers shallow waters near the surf line. While such a location provides an abundance of clean water (and thus food, since shellfish are filter-feeders), the wave action requires a bivalve to glue itself in place or else be swept away.

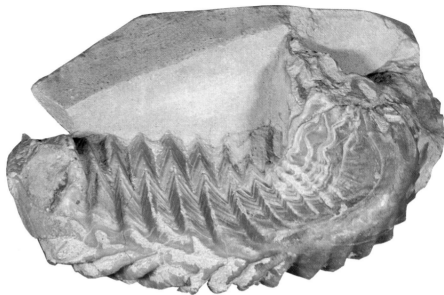

Lopha spp.

TRIASSIC—RECENT

A strongly curved oyster (the specimen shown, L. *carinata*, is seen in profile), *Lopha* valves are thickened, with extremely pronounced ribs that form heavy serrations. The thickening is believed to be a defence against carnivorous gastropods, and is still used by living *Lophas*.

Gervillella spp.

TRIASSIC—CRETACEOUS

Elongated and lanceolate, the valves of *Gervillella* are pointed anteriorly, forming a dagger-like shape, but are unornamented except for concentric growth lines. A medium or large inequivalve, *Gervillella* is found worldwide in appropriate deposits.

Exogyra spp.

CRETACEOUS

A signature species of the Cretaceous, *Exogyra* is an inequivalved fossil of the group loosely known as coiled oysters, which includes *Gryphaea*. As in *Gryphaea*, the left valve is enlarged with a curled umbo, while the right valve is reduced and flat. Species of this genus (which includes the illustrated specimen, E. *latissima*) were sedentary, remaining cemented to the ocean floor.

Exogyra belongs to the group of bivalves known as dysodonts, which all but lack hinge teeth. Shell ornamentation varied.

Venus spp.

OLIGOCENE — RECENT

A large, heavy-shelled clam, *Venus* is oval to circular, with growth lines that form raised, sharp-edged concentric ridges on the circular to oval valves. The species shown is V. *casina* from Pliocene deposits.

The quahog of New England clam chowder fame was once classified with the *Venus* clams, but has since been reassigned to the genus *Mercenaria*.

Spondylus spp.

JURASSIC — RECENT

An extremely widespread fossil genus, *Spondylus* is an inequivalve with regular or irregular costae and, depending upon the species, irregular spines or knobs growing from the costae. The right valve is cemented to the substrata.

One of the most dramatic, living members of this genus is the Atlantic thorny oyster (S. *americanus*), which develops long, delicate spines sometimes more than an inch (2.5 cm) in length.

CLASS **CEPHALOPODA**

Today, the most common cephalopods are octopi and squid, which lack external shells, but during the Palaeozoic and Mesozoic the exquisitely built nautiloids and ammonoids reigned, patrolling the seas in their coiled and chambered ram's-horn shells. Nautiloids and ammonoids are superficially alike, but show several differences. Ammonoid shells, for example, contain more flotation chambers, and the sutures between the chambers are folded into saddles and lobes, unlike the simple sutures of nautiloids. Ammonoid shells usually display one of two kinds of coiling – involute, in which tight outer coils overlap the inner, and evolute, in which looser outer coils do not. Nautiloids and ammonoids grow in a coil because the animal's mantle secretes calcium carbonate at varying rates – more quickly on the sides and outer edges, and less quickly on the dorsal surface closest to the inside of the coil. This is not an accident, of course, but provides the cephalopod with a sturdy, stream-lined refuge.

Nautiloids appeared first in the waning years of the Cambrian, with one surviving species, while the ammonoids arose during the Devonian, and were extinct by the end of the Cretaceous.

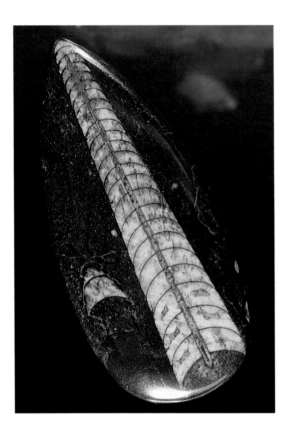

Orthoceras spp.

ORDOVICIAN — TRIASSIC

The most famous of the fossil cephalopods, the nautilus and ammonites, have curved shells, but the Palaeozoic produced many species with straight or only slightly curved shells. One was *Orthoceras*, a large, active predator. This speci-men, from Morocco, shows an *Orthoceras* shell in cross-section. Visible are the septae dividing the body chambers, and the tube-like siphuncle running the length of the shell.

North American orthocerids that had previ-ously been assigned to this genus have been reclassified as several distinct genera.

LEFT *Orthoceras sp.*

Nautilus spp.

OLIGOCENE — RECENT

More than 180 million years old, this fossil *Nautilus* echoes the sole surviving species of its genus, the chambered nautilus. The fossil record contains a much greater diversity of nautiloids. In *Nautilus*, the shell coils up and behind the body chamber like a ram's horn; the live animal, which was tentacled like a squid, protruded from the aperture, and was able to move by jet propulsion, squirting water through a fold of flesh beneath the head. Buoyancy was controlled through gas-filled chambers inside the shell – spaces that had once formed the body chamber, and had been sealed off as the nautilus grew and secreted new sections.

Dactylioceras spp.

JURASSIC

A famous, commonly collected ammonoid of Eurasia, Latin America and parts of North America, Dactylioceras possesses evolute whorls and simple, relatively straight ribs. There is no keel, and the sutures are strongly lobed. The shell is usually four inches (10 cm) in diameter or less.

Shown are three specimens of the species D. *commune*, an important index fossil in European strata, in which the ribs divide over the ventral surface of the whorls. In other members of the Dactylioceras, the ribs remain undivided over the venter, the portion of the whorl farthest from the central axis of the shell.

Hildoceras spp.

JURASSIC

An evolute ammonoid with somewhat flattened whorls, Hildoceras has a shallow groove that runs the length of each side of the whorls as well as along the keel; the ribs are curved. The shell is five inches (12.5 cm) or less in diameter. The specimen illustrated is H. *bifrons*.

ABOVE Dactylioceras commune

LEFT Hildoceras bifrons.

Amaltheus spp.

JURASSIC

Amaltheus belongs to a worldwide group of ammonoids known as ammonitids, a suborder with rather simplistic sutures, heavily ornamented shells and – in some cases – gigantic sizes, with diameters of nearly three feet (1 m). *Amaltheus* itself, however, is much smaller, with an average size of about three inches (7.5 cm). The whorl coiling is involuted, a keel is present, and the ribs form gentle S-shapes. Shown is the species A. *margarinatus*.

Arnioceras spp.

JURASSIC

A common Jurassic ammonoid, *Arnioceras* has strong, straight ribs that curve forward on the venter, stopping at the keel. The coiling is evolute, and the saddles and lobes of the sutures are themselves convoluted into smaller subdivisions. The specimen shown is A. *semicostatum* from the Lower Jurassic, the variety most commonly found.

ABOVE *Arnioceras semicostatum.*

LEFT *Amaltheus margarinatus.*

CLASS **SCAPHOPODA**

Dentalium spp.

ORDOVICIAN—RECENT

Familiar to beachcombers in many parts of the world, the tusk-shells of today are largely indistinguishable from fossilized specimens from the Palaeozoic. The shell is a long, gentle taper, convex or straight and usually ridged, and as the genus and common names suggest, looks very much like a tooth. Modern species live buried in sediment, both inshore and at the edge of the continental shelf.

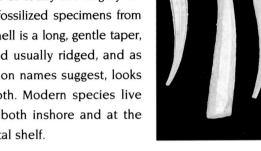

ABOVE Dentalium *sp.*

ARTHROPODS (PHYLUM ARTHROPODA)

Arthropods have segmented, chitinous exoskeletons that are periodically shed as the animal grows, and jointed legs. This phylum, the largest and most diverse in the world (with more than 80 per cent of all living animal species), includes insects, crustaceans, spiders, scorpions and centipedes. The trilobites, an extraordinarily successful subphylum, became extinct during the Permian.

CLASS **TRILOBITA**

Extinct for roughly 250 million years, the trilobites were one of the dominant forms of life in their day, which stretched from the Cambrian to the Permian. The name trilobite comes from the body's three-fold shape. In cross-section, it has a central axis and riblike pleurae jutting out to each side, and lengthwise it has the cephalon (head shield), thorax (body) and pygidium (tail section). Even to those generally unfamiliar with fossils, the trilobite is almost instantly recognizable. The cephalon is usually rounded, with eyes and back-curving spikes known as genal spines; a raised, rounded area at the 'nose' is the glabella. The jointed thorax, with its axis and pleurae, is also distinctive. Most trilobites were oceanic bottom-dwellers, although some species appear to be adapted for swimming actively through open water.

Virtually all trilobite fossils show the hard

dorsal surface of the animal (either as a mould or a cast), and nothing of the underside, which apparently was softer, without calcium carbonate, and thus less likely to fossilize. Despite this, we know that trilobites had paired, jointed appendages for moving, feeding and respiration. The mouth was underneath the cephalon, making it all but certain that trilobites were bottom feeders.

Trilobites first appeared in the Lower Cambrian, diversifying incredibly during the so-called 'Cambrian explosion' some 550 million years BP, when multicellular life itself underwent radical diversification and almost all basic animal body plans appeared.

Scientists ascribe the great number of trilobite fossils to three causes – trilobites possessed exoskeletons armoured with calcium carbonate, which fossilizes easily; most species lived in shallow oceans, where fossilization is most likely to occur; and not the least importantly, they were simply phenomenally common in their day.

ABOVE Calymene blumenbachi.

Calymene spp.

SILURIAN—DEVONIAN

In trilobites, the cephalon is the most important feature for identification. That of *Calymene*, a widespread genus in North America and Europe, is semicircular, while the glabella is raised, convex and has three lobes that taper to the front. The rest of the body tapers to a small, pointed pygidium. The specimen shown is C. *blumenbachi*, from the Silurian, and is just over an inch (2.5 cm) in length.

Flexicalymene spp.

ORDOVICIAN

When a trilobite was threatened or injured, it curled into a tight ball, a process known as enrolling that protected its vulnerable, lightly armoured underside. This specimen of *Flexicalymene retorsa* was fossilized enrolled, a common occurrence with this and many other trilobite genera; it may be that the mud slide that encased them triggered this response, just as bumping a modern wood-louse causes it to enroll as well. Shed exoskeletons of some trilobites also enrolled once they were moulted.

Flexicalymene is easily confused with its close relative *Calymene*, but has a more pronounced cephalon border, and the glabella is larger than the pygidium. *Flexicalymene* is found in parts of Europe, and is especially common in eastern North America.

Niobella spp.

ORDOVICIAN

A mid-sized trilobite, with lengths of up to four inches (10 cm), *Niobella* fossils show a well-developed cephalon, large pygidium and eyes. There are eight thoracic segments. Like all trilobites, *Niobella* (in this case, N. *homfrayi*) was benthic – that is, it spent virtually all its time on the ocean floor, judging from the shape and position of its appendages, as well as its digestive system. Trilobites appear to have been scavengers or hunters, and were probably a combination of both.

Ogygiocarella spp.

ORDOVICIAN

Trilobites of the genus *Ogygiocarella* are common in European and Latin American deposits from the Ordovician. The genus is macropygous – that is, the pygidium is almost as large as the thorax; in addition, the eye is short and curved, the glabella bulges out anteriorly, and the facial suture cuts the rear border of the cephalon. Illustrated are O. *angustissima* and O. *debuchi*, the latter formerly classified as *Ogygia buchi*. Further confusing the issue, the names are sometimes spelled *Ogigiocarella* and *Ogigio*.

TOP O. debuchi.

ABOVE O. augustissima.

ABOVE Elrathia kingii.

Elrathia spp.

CAMBRIAN

A North American trilobite, *Elrathia* is a very important member of the Cambrian fauna, with the species E. *kingii* being especially abundant and widespread. The glabella is short and tapers to the front, with a broad brim and wide free cheeks; the pygidium is small. *Elrathia* belonged to the large group of trilobites called opisthoparians, named for their distinct head sutures. These uncalcified junctures provided the trilobite with an escape route when it had outgrown its exoskeleton, and it was along these lines that the outer shell split when it was time for the trilobite to moult. The opisthoparians were the largest of the trilobites, with some species more than two feet (60 cm) long.

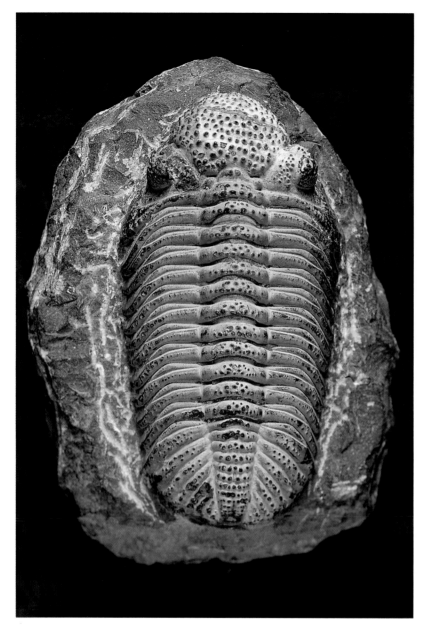

Phacops spp.

SILURIAN—DEVONIAN

The phacopids are the dominant genera of trilobites from middle Palaeozoic rocks in North
America. Phacops rana, shown here, is typical:
the glabella is large and bulbous, wider at the
front than the rear, with at least two pairs of
furrows; the pygidium is the same general
shape as the cephalon, with 10 to 12 segments.
Broken and incomplete fossils, usually of
moulted pieces of exoskeletons, are the most
common Phacops specimens.

Like Phacops, trilobite fossils usually show
large, well-developed eyes, which in this genus
were especially pronounced. Fossil trilobite

eyes retain the faceted surface that in life was
a compound lens, a system found in many
modern arthropods and providing excellent
vision. The eyes of the Phacops were so large
and high that the animal probably enjoyed a
360-degree field of vision.

Asaphiscus spp.

SILURIAN—DEVONIAN

A trademark trilobite from the middle Cambrian,
Asaphiscus is found in deposits in the western
United States. The cephalon and pygidium both
have wide, flattened borders that are distinctive, with a secondary border in front of the
glabella, which has three pairs of furrows. There
are between 7 and 11 thoracic segments in this
genus, and between five and eight segments
on the pygidium. The species shown is the
common A. wheeleri.

CLASS INSECTA

Insects first appeared in the Devonian, the
ancient precursors of today's wingless silver-
fish and springtails. Gaps in the fossil record
make sorting out the sequence difficult, but by
the Carboniferous, dragonflies – the earliest
winged insects – had taken to the air. With no
competition from other flying animals, these
early dragonflies were massive, with wingspans
of nearly three feet (1 m).

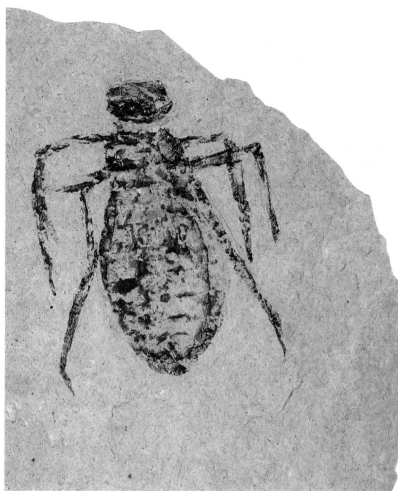

Insect trapped in amber

OLIGOCENE

Nearly 40 million years ago, on what is now the island of Dominica, this small insect became trapped in tree resin. Mired and eventually entombed, it quickly died of suffocation, and the complete lack of oxygen that killed it also prevented bacteria from decomposing it. Eventually the resin fossilized into amber, preserving the insect – a member of the *Hymenoptera*, the large order that includes ants, wasps and bees.

Even though the insect appears to be intact, down to the tiniest details of antennae and wing veins, it is really a hollow mould in the resin, around the edges of which clings a thin, carbonized film. To the observer, however, the amber provides a perfect window to a death many millions of years in the past.

Libellula doris spp.

MIOCENE

Insects are rare as fossils, partly because of their thin, easily destroyed exoskeletons. This dragonfly larva is one of the unusual exceptions, perhaps because its habitat – probably ponds or slow-moving rivers with mud bottoms, as in living species – is more conducive to fossilization than the terrestrial environments inhabited by most insects. The dragonfly family *Libellulidae* remains widespread today, and includes the familiar Common Skimmer of North America.

ABOVE
LEFT Libellula doris
(dragonfly larva).
ABOVE Hymenoptera *in
amber.*

CLASS **CRUSTACEA**

Crustaceans evolved at around the same point in the Cambrian as the trilobites, but apparently were held in check by their vastly more successful arthropod relatives. The mass extinctions of the trilobites at the end of the Permian, however, left the niches they once occupied empty, and the crustaceans radiated to fill most of those ecological slots.

Notopocrystes spp.

CRETACEOUS

The carapace of crabs and other crustaceans – that is, the shieldlike covering on the thorax and head – is often the only body part to survive fossilization. In the Mesozoic crab *Notopocrystes*, the carapace is oval or shield-shaped, covered with tiny bumps and featuring a series of knobs that form a low dorsal ridge. Illustrated is the species N. *stokesi*, a specimen from England, although this genus (sometimes listed as *Palaeocorystes*) is found in Europe, North America, parts of the Middle East and Indo-Pacific.

Xanthopsis spp.

EOCENE

Crustaceans usually do not appear as fossils in the abundance that brachiopods, trilobites and molluscs achieve, but *Xanthopsis* is an exception. Plentiful in Eocene deposits in North America and Europe, it and related genera sometimes form thick beds made up almost exclusively of their fossilized carapaces.

Xanthopsis was a stout crab about two inches (5 cm) across, similar in shape to the rock and mud crabs that live today along the coast of New England. The claws were thick and strong, held close to the body, as can be seen in this specimen of X. *leachi*, which shows the crab's underside. The carapace was oval and convex, with distinct furrows.

ECHINODERMS (PHYLUM ECHINODERMATA)

The name echinoderm means 'spiny skin', an apt description for many of this phylum's members, which include sea urchins, sea stars, sea cucumbers and crinoids. All are built on a body plan that is based on multiples of five, which covers everything from the number of arms to the branches of the vascular system. They have been entirely marine through their history. Several extinct classes, the blastoids among them, are important fossils.

CLASS **CRINOIDAE (CRINOIDS)**

Divers know the living crinoids as 'sea lilies', since they bear a resemblance to plants, with their sinuous stalks and feathery, petal-like arms. Fossil crinoids are varied and beautiful if found intact, although many are only fragments of the ossicles (stem segments) or the cupped calyx, the body. In some weathered deposits, crinoid ossicles litter the ground like stone buttons.

Fossils can tell a palaeontologist only so much, and comparisons with living forms – when possible – can provide valuable insight into extinct genera. Fossil beds provide little on crinoid life history, for instance, but we know from studying modern crinoids that the larvae are mobile before settling down. Interestingly, even crinoids that are stalkless as adults go through a stalked larval phase; such a replaying of ancestral forms in juvenile stages is common, and its study is an important tool for deciphering the past. Even human beings, for example, go through a stage in which the embryos have gill pouches and a fishlike tail.

impressions of the pinnules, the smaller, branching armlets, as well as the clasping stem branchlets known as cirri. The pinnules, covered in sticky mucous, served as filtering devices for the crinoid, capturing plankton from the water and transferring it to the animal's calyx.

ABOVE Cyathocrinites arthiticus.

Cyathocrinites spp.

SILURIAN—CARBONIFEROUS

A common Palaeozic crinoid, *Cyathocrinites* had a globular calyx and branching arms composed of a single row of plates, as can be seen in this specimen of C. *arthriticus*, from the Silurian. Stalked crinoids like *Cyathocrinites* were dominant in the ancient seas of the Palaeozoic, but in plankton-poor modern oceans they have been largely replaced by stalkless, mobile genera that arose in the Mesozoic. Stalked crinoids are today found only on deep reefs in tropical regions.

Pentacrinites spp.

TRIASSIC—RECENT

In this piece of shale, the long arms, or branches, of *Pentacrinites* have been preserved, along with

BELOW Pentacrinites *sp.*

Apiocrinus spp.

JURASSIC

This specimen of *Apiocrinus*, the species A. *parkinsoni*, shows the genus' teardrop-shaped calyx, composed of the radial, basal and ray plates fused almost seamlessly with the upper ossicles. Fossils of this genus are found only in Europe.

Botryocrinus spp.

SILURIAN

Crinoids were far more successful than their close relatives, the cystoids and blastoids, outnumbering them nearly five to one in terms of fossil genera, with a total of more than 750. In addition, only the crinoids survived the mass extinctions at the end of the Permian. This specimen of *Botryocrinus*, from the Wenlock Limestones, is Silurian.

Marsupites spp.

CRETACEOUS

All echinoderms show five-fold radial symmetry in their body plans, and that is no less true of *Marsupites*. The calyx is made up of three rows of five plates each, all heavily scored with radial ridging. Found in North American and European deposits, *Marsupites* was a stalkless, free-swimming crinoid. The specimen shown is M. *testudinarius*.

Glyptocrinus spp.

ORDOVICIAN—SILURIAN

This specimen of a Silurian *Glyptocrinus* shows the long stalk, arms and branching pinnules, but unfortunately not much of the calyx, which in this genus is conical, with radial ridges. *Glyptocrinus* fossils can be found in both North America and Europe.

CLASS **ECHINOIDAE (SEA URCHINS, SAND DOLLARS AND ALLIES)**

This class is marked by the presence of a central, boxlike test composed of hard plates fused together to form 10 bands that radiate from the top. The body is covered with spines, although in most fossils only the test is preserved. The test is usually globular or flattened, although conical species occur.

The large opening on the underside of the test in echinoids is known as the peristome, which contains the mouth. The 'jaws' in echinoids are made up of five pointed, calcareous plates with the non-technical name of Aristotle's lantern, for their fancied resemblance to an old lamp. Ancient lighting has provided names for a surprising number of animals, including brachiopods (lampshells) and a group of fossil sponges.

grooves – the five zones between the rows of tubercules – are ornamented with regular rows of tiny tubercules. The ambulacral grooves move food to the oral opening underneath the test, while the anus is found at the periproct, the cluster of small, central plates at the top of the test. The species illustrated is H. *intermedia*.

Pygurus spp.

CRETACEOUS—EOCENE

The star-shaped ambulacral grooves make *Pygurus* instantly recognizable as a 'sand dollar', the common name for the tests of flattened, short-spined sea urchins. Many similar genera survive in the world's oceans, delighting beachcombers. The edges of the ambulacral grooves are studded with pores, through which tube feet protruded, permitting the animal to breathe and move. In life, *Pygurus* would probably have been buried slightly in sand, allowing wave action to bring food particles to it.

Hemicidaris spp.

JURASSIC—CRETACEOUS

The widespread fossil sea urchin is usually preserved as the test alone. The test is knobbed with tubercules like a floating mine, and these become larger as they approach the underside. The test is a flattened sphere, especially so on the venter. The ambulacral

Micraster spp.

CRETACEOUS—PALAEOCENE

Echinoids can be regular (those that are radially symmetrical) or irregular (those in which the test shape is bilaterally symmetrical). *Micraster*, a common European echinoid, is irregular; the test is heart-shaped, with short ambulacral plates. A groove leads from the centre of the test to the oral opening on the side, with a low ridge running the opposite direction, towards the posterior, where the anus is located. This genus (represented here by M. *coranguinum*) is used to identify Cretaceous strata in Europe.

Echinocorys spp.

CRETACEOUS

Seen in profile, the test of *Echinocorys* is high, rounded and flat on the venter. The ambulacral grooves are widely separated, with double rows of pores on the slightly granular test. The genus is widespread in North America and Eurasia. The species shown is E. *scutata*.

Plegiocidaris spp.

JURASSIC

Generally speaking, each genus of echinoid has a distinctive spine shape that helps in identification – but the shapes can seem whimsical to the human eye, like that of *Plegiocidaris*, which looks more than a little like an ear of corn. *Plegiocidaris* is usually found with other inhabitants of ancient coral reefs, and it serves as an environmental indicator fossil, especially if found with other echinoids that shared its taste for warm, shallow seawater. The species illustrated is P. *florigemme*.

CLASS BLASTOIDAE (BLASTOIDS)

Similar to cystoids, the blastoids possessed a globular or budshaped theca, usually the only part of the animal to be fossilized.

Pentremites spp.

CARBONIFEROUS — PERMIAN

A Western Hemisphere speciality, *Pentremites* is one of the best-known and most common blastoids in North America. The theca is globular to budshaped, with five distinct ambulacral grooves extending from the mouth down the sides towards the base. In life, blastoids probably resembled delicate crinoids, anchored to the sea bed by thin stalks, and seining plankton from the water with the help of waving, mucous-covered arms.

Judging from fossil deposits, blastoids like *Pentremites* inhabited the reef front, where wave action is greatest. Other genera may have been more mobile, able to float from spot to spot, then anchor themselves temporarily with prehensile holdfasts.

CLASS CYSTOIDAE (CYSTOIDS)

These stemmed echinoderms resembled crinoids to an extent, and possessed globular theca with plates that numbered between a few dozen and more than 1,000. Cystoids were sessile and apparently fixed. An extinct class, they arose during the Ordovician and died out by the end of the Devonian.

CLASS ASTEROIDAE (SEA STARS)

Often incorrectly called 'star fish', sea stars are active bottom-dwellers, most capable of movement on tiny, tubular feet. Sea stars do not fossilize well, and are therefore rare as fossils. Another class of stars, the *Ophiuroidae*, contains the brittle stars, which are also infrequent as fossils.

CLASS GRAPTOLTHINA (GRAPTOLITES)
PHYLUM (*HEMICHORDATA*)

These extinct colonial animals have left behind delicately beautiful fossils that resemble branches of coral. The colony, or rhabdosome, is made up of stipes, or branches, which are in turn marked by small depressions called thecae, in which the animals lived; thecae may be small (bithecae) or bigger (autothecae). The rhabdosomes were themselves part of a larger cluster jutting out from a buoyant nematophore. It is believed that graptolite colonies floated near the surface or anchored themselves to floating debris, although some of the earliest forms were apparently bottom-dwellers. The majority of the following graptolites are found worldwide.

Graptolites are most common in black shales, and are, ironically, among the very few fossils ever found in such rocks, which were formed in an almost oxygen-free environment, toxic with hydrogen sulphide, in which nothing could live. If graptolites were bottom-dwellers as first thought, how could they survive without oxygen? Yet, if they were planktonic, why weren't they found in other strata? The answer seems to be that their protein-based exoskeleton was simply too easily decomposed anywhere except in the harsh, poisonous environment that went on to produce the black shales, although some graptolites have been found in limestone.

Graptolites long confused palaeontologists, who weren't sure if they were plants or animals – and if animals, whether they belonged with the sponges, the bryozoans, the molluscs or the cnidarians. Finally, microscopic examination showed them to be protochordates – the group that later gave rise to vertebrates.

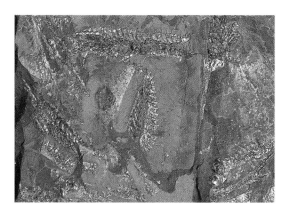

Phyllograptus spp.

ORDOVICIAN

The *Phyllograptus* rhabdosome has four joined stipes, creating an X-shape when sectioned. The thecae of this genus are tubular and simplistic. Like most graptolites, the stipes are thinner than a pencil lead.

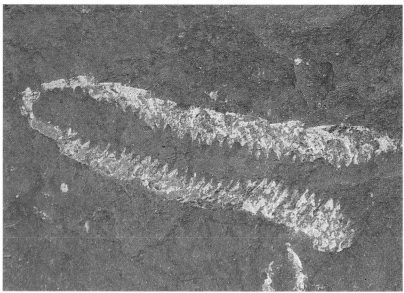

Didymograptus spp.

ORDOVICIAN

This specimen of D. *murchinsoni* displays the characteristic shape of the genus, in which the stipes are folded together like tongs. Occasionally they will have been fossilized in a straight line. The thecae are pronounced and toothlike, on the insides of the stipe like serrations on a pair of pinking shears.

Tetragraptus spp.

ORDOVICIAN

Sadly, fossilization is rarely kind to graptolites, which are usually preserved as squashed, carbonized films with little or no three-dimensional detail, with the stipes often torn and scattered. Most graptolite fossils are similar to the specimen of *Tetragraptus* shown here, but in those in a better state of preservation, the rhabdosomes are made up of four stipes, joined as pairs. The thecae are straight and sawtoothed. In life, the stipes hung from a threadlike support called the nema, arching up and out like the leaves of a ground-hugging flower.

Orthograptus spp.

ORDOVICIAN — SILURIAN

Unlike *Didymograptus*, *Orthograptus* belongs to the biserial graptolites – those with rows of thecae on both sides of the stipe, instead of just one. The colony consisted of a single stipe, suspended from a thin nema (a short length of which also fossilized in this specimen); the thecae pointed upwards at a 45-degree angle.

Climacograptus spp.

ORDOVICIAN—SILURIAN

Large, squared-off thecae mark *Climacograptus*, another biserial graptolite with a single stipe. Oval body parts found with *Climacograptus* are thought to have been flotation buoys, from which the colony was suspended.

Monograptus spp.

SILURIAN—DEVONIAN

A close-up of a *Monograptus* stipe shows the tightly packed, uniserial thecae. This is a highly variable genus, with stipe and thecae shape ranging from straight to gracefully curved. *Monograptus* is one of the most commonly found of the graptolites.

Rastrites spp.

SILURIAN

With their curved stipes and long thecae, *Rastrites* colonies lok a little bit like ancient false eyelashes. The thecae are uniserial and are themselves slightly curved, and are more widely spaced than most graptolite thecae.

VERTEBRATES

CLASS CHONDRICHTHYES (CARTILAGINOUS FISH)

The first protofish arose roughly 540 million years BP, around the cusp of the Cambrian and Ordovician, and their jawless descendants reached their zenith during the Devonian before fading away. They were replaced by two groups of fish – the cartilaginous fish, which today includes sharks and rays, and the more advanced bony fish. Cartilaginous fish have skeletons made of tough, flexible cartilage. While this may seem a primitive trait, the *Chondrichthyes* appear to have evolved from bony ancestors. The most frequently fossilized parts of sharks and rays are their teeth, which can be found in astounding numbers in some areas.

Odontaspis spp.

J U R A S S I C — R E C E N T

The sand sharks of the genus *Odontaspis* possess long, curved teeth that are often found along ocean beaches; Florida is particularly noted for its aggregations of fossil shark teeth. Because of abrasion in the surf, the bases are frequently worn away, but when intact, there are usually small, auxiliary spines protruding from the top of the base on either side of the tooth.

While *Odontaspis* and its relatives were common in Cenozoic seas, the numbers of fossilized teeth may give a skewed idea of their abundance. Sharks lose their teeth constantly throughout their lives, with replacements constantly migrating forward from rows of backup teeth, so one shark can produce hundreds.

Carcharodon spp.

C R E T A C E O U S — R E C E N T

The large size, triangular shape and serrated edges of this tooth mark it as belonging to *Carcharodon megalodon*, a Cenozoic relative of the modern great white shark. By comparing the size of teeth from C. *megalodon* to proportions of living great whites, it was once thought the extinct species grew to lengths of more than 90 feet (27.5 m), and would have been capable of swallowing a small car. Those estimates are now known to be wrong, but C. *megalodon* was nonetheless at least 50 feet (15 m) long – certainly one of the most formidable predators history has ever produced.

CLASS OSTEICHYTHYES (BONY FISH)

Far and away the most successful class of fish in modern waters, bony fish first appeared in the Devonian. Not long after, they split into two evolutionary lines; one produced the world's more than 20,000 species of typical bony fish, the other the lungfishes and lobefins, including the famous coelacanths of the genus *Latimeria*. It is thought that this second group gave rise to the amphibians, the first land vertebrates.

Gosnitichthys spp.

EOCENE

The Green River shales of Wyoming are justly famous for the quantity and quality of the bony fish fossils they produce. In this example, a school of small G. *paruns* have been fossilized as they died, perhaps the victims of depleted dissolved oxygen, which still causes massive fish kills, or a drought. The alignment of many of the fish also indicates a possible water current, or the action of waves, before the fish were buried.

Acanthonemus spp.

TERTIARY

This fossil fish, a rarity in Tertiary strata, appears to be related to the pompanos and crevalles, and is classified with the Perciformes. The species shown is A. *subaureus*; the genus is found from the Eocene to the Oligocene in European strata.

Prolates spp.

TERTIARY

Prolates is one of the earliest examples of the order *Perciformes*, which is today the largest order of vertebrates in the world. It includes such familiar fish as the sunfish, bass, darters, pike and true perches. The specimen shown is P. *herberti*, found in early Palaeocene strata in France.

ABOVE Gosnitichthys paruns.

Lepidotus spp.

CRETACEOUS

Lepidotus was a member of the group of bony fishes known as semionotids, heavily built fish with small mouths, simple, peglike teeth and thick scales. The group arose during the Permian and became common in marine deposits during the Jurassic, but none survived the great extinction at the K-T Boundary. These round objects are fossilized vertebrae from L. *marimus*, a species that lived in the Cretaceous, just before the genus died out forever. By examining *Lepidotus* teeth, palaeontologists believe this and other related genera fed on heavily shelled invertebrates.

LEFT Lepidotus marimus vertebrae.

Latimeria spp.

DEVONIAN – RECENT

The coelacanth (as this genus is popularly known) was believed extinct for 70 million years until one was pulled up by a trawler off the coast of South Africa in 1938. Many more have been caught since then, most from the Comoro Islands and all from great depths. This preserved, modern specimen shows the hallmarks of its fossil ancestors – most importantly the lobelike fins, which were supported internally by bones and could act as primitive limbs. The lobefins also had primitive lungs that would have allowed them to breathe on land. It is important to realize that *Latimeria* itself is only an offshoot of this once-diverse group, and while it retains the family's structure, it is not the direct ancestor of the first land vertebrates.

CLASS **AMPHIBIA (AMPHIBIANS)**

The first vertebrates to dominate the land were the amphibians, which held sway for nearly 50 million years, beginning in the late Devonian and reaching their peak in the Carboniferous. Amphibians have moist, scaleless skin and lay eggs coated in a gelatinous substance, without a watertight shell. The eggs must be laid in water or in a very damp place, largely restricting this class to humid or semi-aquatic environments.

Micromelerpeton spp.

PERMIAN

Not long after the amphibians evolved, they split into two major groups. One, the labyrinthodonts, eventually gave rise to the reptiles, while the other, the temnospondyls, remained an evolutionary dead-end, flourishing from the Permian through the Triassic, then eventually dying out. *Micromelerpeton* was a member of the latter group, in the suborder *Rhachitomi*. Like many early amphibians it had a wide, flat head, short limbs held splayed out to the side, and a low, waddling carriage. The species shown is M. *amphibia*, a specimen from Lower Permian deposits in Germany.

BELOW Micromelerpeton amphibia.

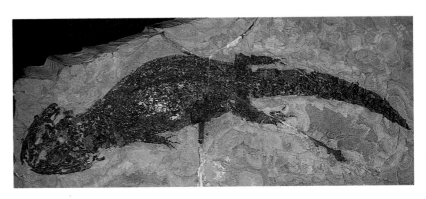

CLASS **REPTILIA (REPTILES)**

The most famous fossil reptiles – indeed, the best-known fossils of all – are the dinosaurs. While reptiles had evolved as early as the Devonian, dinosaurs themselves did not arrive on the scene until the Triassic, many millions of years later. Today, in fact, there is great debate over whether dinosaurs truly belong in the *Reptilia* at all. It has always been assumed that dinosaurs shared the typical reptilian trait of ectothermy ('cold-bloodedness'), a sluggish metabolism dependent on external temperature. But recent research indicates that they may instead have been active, warm-blooded creatures with insulating coats of fur or feathers. To some scientists, there is a clear case for reclassifying dinosaurs with their warm-blooded descendants, the birds, in a new class called *Dinosauria*.

Stenopterygius quadriscissus

JURASSIC

Judging from their relative abundance in Jurassic marine deposits, the group of fishlike dinosaurs known as ichthyosaurs (which included *Stenopterygius*) must have been the pre-eminent vertebrates of the middle Mesozoic seas. They were superbly streamlined, as can be easily seen in this extremely well-preserved specimen, which shows the outline of the soft parts surrounding the skeleton – the high dorsal fin, stabilizing flippers and forked tail flukes. Ichthyosaur teeth are commonly found, and can be distinguished by their deep lateral grooves; the teeth have barrel-shaped roots and are set into grooves in the jawbones. The skull tapers drastically beyond the cranial cavity, as does a modern dolphin's skull. In fact, the similarities in appearance between this extinct dinosaur and the living, mammalian dolphins are an excellent example of evolutionary convergence, in which two unrelated animals adapt in similar ways to similar environments.

Pterodactylus spp.

JURASSIC — CRETACEOUS

The first of the flying reptiles to come to light, this small species was discovered in a German quarry and described by Baron Georges Cuvier, the great, pioneering palaeontologist of the early nineteenth century. Noting its elongated front digit, he named it *Pterodactylus*, meaning 'wing-finger'. Even though this species was the first pterodactyl discovered, it was a late-comer in the history of this varied group, which included long- and short-tailed species, and head shapes that ranged from the tapered jaws of the *Pterodactylus*, to blunt triangles and even an upcurved beak fitted with filter plates, which may have functioned much as a flamingo's beak to strain plankton. Most were relatively small, but one, named *Quetzalcoatlus* after the Aztec feathered snake god, may have had a wingspan of more than 50 feet (15 m).

Lufengosaurus

TRIASSIC — JURASSIC

The earliest and most primitive of the large dinosaurs, the prosauropods (or anchisaurids, as many now prefer) were ancestors, indirectly, of the much more massive sauropods. Between 5 and 40 feet (1.5 and 12 m) long, they had long tails and moderately long necks, although neither end of the animal was tapered to the extreme that sauropods would exhibit. Although probably four-footed most of the time, it is reasonable to assume that anchisaurids were able to rear up on their hind legs for feeding, using the tail as a brace. Another clue to their posture is found on the front legs, which are armed with curved claws. Such weapons, while modest by the standards of later dinosaurs like *Triceratops*, would have been effective against attackers, especially if the anchisaurid stood upright. The variety shown is *Lufengosaurus*, a prosauropod of about 20 feet (6 m) in length. Like its relatives, it fed on low vegetation, rising up to nibble at leaves 10 or 15 feet (3 or 6 m) above the ground.

Shuosaurus

JURASSIC

The sauropods, the famous clan that included *Diplodicus* and *Apatosaurus*, were big dinosaurs, with one species that may have been more than 100 feet (30 m) long. But not every sauropod was a giant; *Shuosaurus*, discovered in Asia, was only about 30 feet (9 m) long, and was one of the earliest sauropods to evolve.

Shuosaurus, as this mounted skeleton shows, had an impressive set of teeth. Although they may appear long and predatory, they are actually designed for cropping and chewing vegetation. By examining the wear patterns of sauropod teeth, some palaeontologists have challenged the long-held view that these were swamp-dwellers eating soft aquatic vegetation. In many species, the teeth show the kind of abrasion usually associated with tough land plants like conifer needles, lending strength to the argument that sauropods were terrestrial browsers with a lifestyle more like giraffes than hippos.

ABOVE *Mounted* Shuosarus *skeleton.*

Mamenchisaurus

JURASSIC

With 19 neck vertebrae, *Mamenchisaurus* holds the record for the longest neck among the dinosaurs, and perhaps in the whole animal kingdom. This Asian dinosaur belonged to the group known as diplodocids, the long-tailed, long-necked browsers, of which *Apatosaurus* (formerly *Brontosaurus*) is the most famous.

Despite its prize-winning neck, *Mamenchisaurus* was not the longest diplodocid; at about 70 feet (21 m), it was exceeded by several other species with total lengths of more than 90 feet (27 m). Old reconstructions depicted this group as semi-aquatic, using their long necks as periscopes in deep water; the theory held that only in water could so large a beast support itself. As part of the recent revision in thinking about dinosaurs, the diplodocids and their relatives are now thought to have been land animals, capable of rearing back on their hind legs (braced by their tails) to feed in the highest branches of the coniferous forests that covered the landscape.

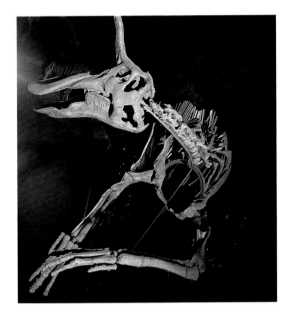

Tsintaosaurus

CRETACEOUS

Some controversy surrounds the reconstructions of this Chinese dinosaur, one of the hadrosaurids, or duckbill dinosaurs. Hadrosaurids were herbivores with flat, almost beak-like mouths apparently designed for browsing low-growing trees and shrubs, but what is most remarkable about them are their head ornaments – crests, spikes and tubes of every description.

In most of the other hadrosaurs, the crests point back, but specimens of the 30-foot (9 m) *Tsintaosaurus* have been mounted with the bony crest sticking straight out, giving the animal the appearance of a unicorn. A more logical position, some palaeontologists believe, would be for the crest to point back, as in *Tsintaosaurus'* relatives.

The duckbills have been the focus of renewed study in recent years, centring on social behaviour in dinosaurs. While such knowledge may seem impossible to gain from fossils, scientists examining the head crests now believe they may have served as resonating chambers for mating songs. The discovery of fossil duckbill nests, all spaced exactly one duckbill-length from each other, suggests that females incubated their eggs, keeping just out of pecking range of the other females, like seabird colonies today.

Tuojiangosaurus

JURASSIC

The stegosaurs were a varied group of herbivorous dinosaurs in the Jurassic and Cretaceous, best known for *Stegosaurus*, with its double row of bony plates running down the back. There were many other genera, however, whose fossils have been found across the Northern Hemisphere, India and Africa. *Tuojiangosaurus* is another recent find from the fertile deposits in China, source of so many new dinosaur discoveries. Somewhat smaller than the 30-foot (9 m) *Stegosaurus*, it bore twin rows of spiky plates and a double pair of tail spines.

There is a great deal of disagreement over the correct placement (and function) of the stegosaurs' back plates. Some palaeontologists see them as a strictly defensive adaptation, while others argue for their role in a heat-regulation system, much as a jack rabbit's outsized ears shed excess body heat.

Scolosaurus

CRETACEOUS

Fossilized dinosaur skin is rare, and provides an invaluable glimpse of their appearance and – to a great degree – lifestyle. This fossil skin impression is from *Scolosaurus*, one of the anky-losaurs known as nodosaurids – squat, barrel-bodied dinosaurs with short legs, broad backs and long tails. They were among the most heavily armoured of living things, and are usually compared to tanks; the upper surface of the body was sheathed in strong plates, and many species grew thick spines around the perimeter of the body and down the tail. *Scolo-saurus* grew to about 12 feet (3.5 m), and lived in what is now North America.

Nodosaurids were only one of many groups of dinosaurs in the Cretaceous that specialized in browsing ground-level plants – a major shift in feeding strategy from the long-necked feed-ers that predominated in the Jurassic. To some experts, the change reflects the growing import-ance of flowering plants in the ecosystem, which were then replacing the gymnosperms in many niches.

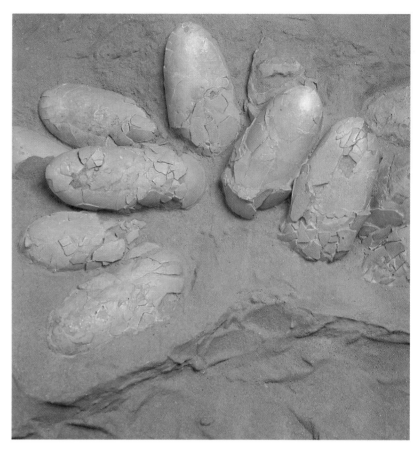

ABOVE Protoceratops *eggs.*

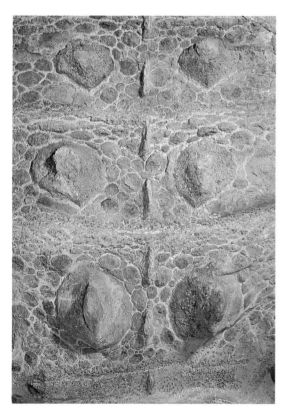

LEFT *Fossilized* Scolosaurus *skin.*

Protoceratops spp.

CRETACEOUS

The discovery of the first dinosaur eggs, in 1923 by the Andrews expedition to central Asia, captured world attention. Further field work has since shown the eggs of *Protoceratops* to be surprisingly common in the Gobi Desert, sug-gesting that this predecessor of the horned dinosaurs (like *Triceratops*) was an abundant dinosaur in the Asian Cretaceous.

The eggs are usually found in circular group-ings inside the remains of the hollow scrape that served as a nest. The adult *Protoceratops* was less massively built than its later relatives, without the exaggerated horns (just a knob on the end of the snout), and only a small head shield. This defence was not always adequate; in the 1970s, another Gobi Desert expedition turned up the skeleton of a *Protoceratops* locked with that of a *Velociraptor*, an agile, birdlike predatory dinosaur. Apparently the *Protoceratops* managed to kill its attacker, even as it was be-ing disemboweled by the *Velociraptor*'s hind talons.

LEFT Gasosaurus, *an ancestor of* Tyrannosaurus.

Gasosaurus

JURASSIC

The theropods began as small, meat-eating dinosaurs in the Triassic, and eventually produced the reigning carnivores of the 'Age of Dinosaurs': *Allosaurus* in the Jurassic and *Tyrannosaurus* in the Cretaceous. *Gasosaurus* was a much smaller theropod, but was built along the same lines as its more notorious relatives – large, powerful hind legs, comparatively tiny forelegs adapted for grasping, a long tail to counterbalance the body while running, and a mouth armed with curving, knifelike teeth.

Triceratops spp.

CRETACEOUS

It was one of the great confrontations of prehistory: the towering, predatory dinosaur *Tyrannosaurus* against the tanklike, heavily armoured herbivore *Triceratops*. *Triceratops'* weaponry was formidable, to say the least: two curved, sharp horns angling forward from just above the eyes, with a third, shorter horn on the snout. The vulnerable neck was protected by a wide head shield that flared back several feet, and was rimmed with short spikes.

Although *Triceratops* is the much better known, there were many other horned dinosaurs of the middle and late Cretaceous, some with even more bizarre head ornamentation. *Torosaurus* and *Pentaceratops* had greatly expanded head shields, while an earlier genera, *Stycosaurus*, sported only a long nose horn on its face, but a half-dozen more that rose out of the edge of its head shield.

CLASS **AVES (BIRDS)**

Birds first appear in the fossil record during the Jurassic with *Archaeopteryx*, an obvious intermediary between small, fast-moving dinosaurs like *Deinonychus* and true birds; in fact, *Archaeopteryx* fits just as well among the dinosaurs as it does among birds, and one specimen was misidentified for years as a pterodactyl.

In order to fly, birds have hollow, thinly walled bones that rarely fossilize, so that their history is spotty. From the fossils that have been found, however, we know that by the Cretaceous, toothed birds with fully functional wings had evolved, followed by wholly modern birds at the Cretaceous-Palaeocene border.

Archaeopteryx

JURASSIC

First there was a feather – a startling imprint found in Germany in 1860, from Jurassic rock where dinosaurs, not birds, were expected. Less than a year later, the same limestone of the fabled Solnhofen quarries in Bavaria had given up a nearly complete *Archaeopteryx* fossil, riveting world attention. This exceedingly fine-grained limestone, perfect for lithographic plates, is also nearly perfect for fossilization, preserving details that would be lost in a coarser matrix. So it was with *Archaeopteryx*, which could be seen to have a dinosaur-like skeleton, a long, bony tail and reptile-like teeth. And as the limestone clearly showed, *Archaeopteryx* also had feathers.

The fossil illustrated is the famous 'Berlin Specimen', unearthed in 1877. The head, with its toothed mouth, is flung backwards, while impressions of the wing and tail feathers are easily seen. The three long 'finger' bones in *Archaeopteryx* eventually degenerated into the three small, partially fused digits found in modern birds.

Today, the biggest question is how powered flight developed, be it by *Archaeopteryx*, its predecessors or its descendants. It is by no means clear that *Archaeopteryx* flew (or at least flew well). An established theory holds that such primitive birds evolved flight feathers to facilitate gliding, while others argue that flight grew from leaps by fast-running dinosaurs, like many of *Archaeopteryx*' close relatives. Proponents of warm-bloodedness among dinosaurs see the feathers as further proof, since cold-blooded reptiles have no need of insulation.

LEFT Archaeopteryx, *and above, reconstruction from fossil evidence.*

CLASS **MAMMALIA (MAMMALS)**

Our own class, the *Mammalia* is wonderfully diverse, encompassing everything from whales to bats to gorillas – all united by warm-bloodedness, body hair and the production of milk for the young. Mammals first evolved about 215 million years BP, apparently arising from a group of mammal-like reptiles known as theraspids during the Triassic. Initially, mammals laid eggs (a reproductive process still used by echidnas and the platypus), while a later group, the marsupials, gave birth to scarcely developed young called neonates, retained in a nursing pouch for months thereafter. The marsupials' spot at the top was eventually usurped by modern, placental mammals everywhere but in Australia and, until the middle Cenozoic, South America.

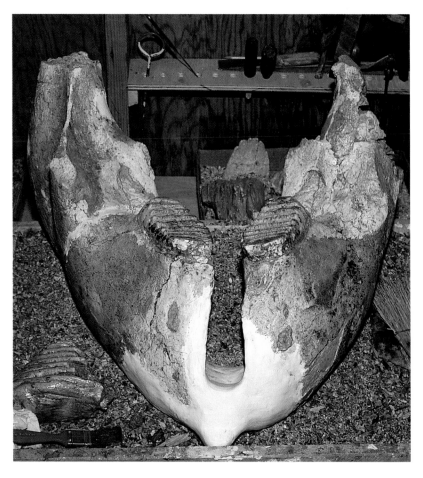

Mammuthus spp.

OLIGOCENE — PLEISTOCENE

By the Pleistocene, mammoths and mastodons were found all over the Northern Hemisphere, Africa and South America. The smaller mastodons survived in North America until after the last glaciers retreated, and were hunted by Palaeolithic Indians less than 10,000 years ago.

The proboscidians, including the elephants, arose in the late Eocene or early Oligocene, first in the form of piglike creatures known as *Moeritherium*. Over time, the snout elongated into the famous trunk, while the jaw shortened and the teeth were reduced to only eight active molars in modern elephants, with two upper incisors (not canines, as often supposed) transformed into tusks. The gigantic steppe mammoth (M. *trogontherii*) was the largest European elephant, with a shoulder height of more than 14 feet (4 m), and tusks more than 16 feet (5 m) long. The photo, showing a jaw of North America's M. *columbi* from South Dakota, demonstrates the size of these extinct mammals.

Woolly mammoths (M. *primigenius*) from Siberia and Alaska have provided some of the most unique fossils in palaeontological history – almost perfectly frozen specimens from the Pleistocene, many still with mouthfuls of grass and wildflowers. In some cases the mammoths were so well-preserved that the meat was still edible. Tusks are often uncovered during gold mining operations, and form the basis for a lucrative trade in fossil ivory.

LEFT *Lower jaw of* Mammuthus columbi.

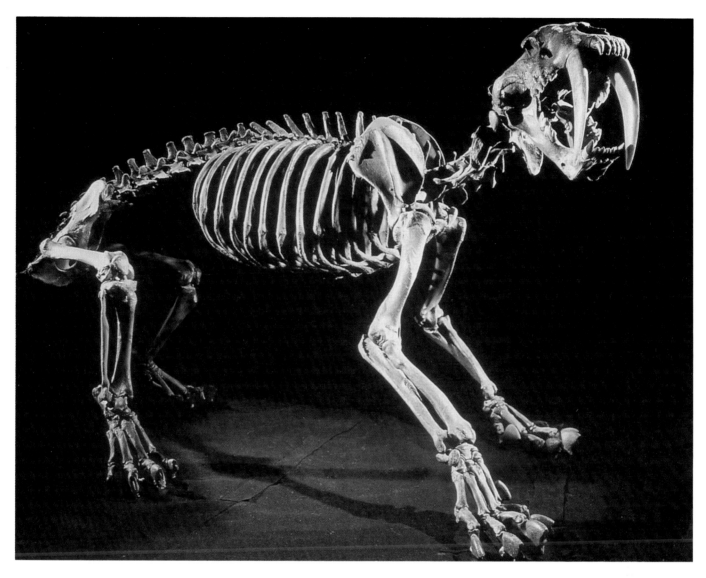

Smilodon spp.

PLEISTOCENE

Popularly known as 'sabre-toothed tigers', these large, unusual cats were apparently common carnivores in North and South America during the Pleistocene. The most startling feature of the skull are the upper canine teeth, which have evolved into sweeping fangs.

The fangs certainly look deadly, and it has long been assumed that *Smilodon* used them to great effect against such thick-skinned prey as mammoths and mastodons; the discovery of sabre-toothed cat skeletons and those of primitive elephants, together in California tar pits, would seem to seal the argument. But others have argued that *Smilodon*'s fangs were too big to be efficient biting tools, and are awkwardly placed for stabbing. They theorize that the cat may have been a scavenger, and the huge teeth might have played a social, rather than predatory, role.

Whatever the function of the sabre-teeth, they must have been effective, for the same style of dentition had evolved earlier, independently, in a South American marsupial known as *Thylacosmilus*, which lived during the Pliocene but died out when the Central American land bridge joined North and South America, permitting a flood of placental mammals to move south. The unique marsupial fauna of South America were overwhelmed by the placentals, and the marsupials largely vanished.

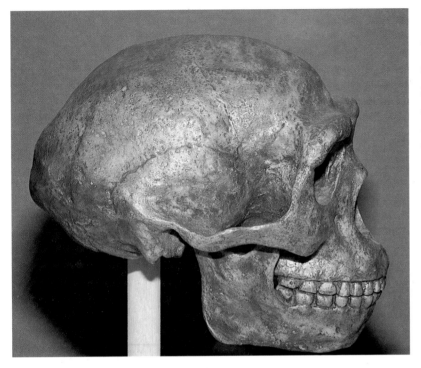

Homo erectus

PLEISTOCENE

Of all the prizes prehistory has to offer the fossil hunter, the fossils of early human beings are the rarest. *Homo erectus* was the direct ancestor of modern man, living across the Old World as early as 1.6 million years BP. The first specimens to come to light, in 1891, were found in Java, followed in the 1920s by the discovery of Peking Man (illustrated here) in China. Both Java Man and Peking Man are known to be of the same species, despite small differences.

Homo erectus skulls exhibit a pronounced brow ridge, low forehead and receding chin, but these were not the stooped, apelike 'cavemen' of popular conception. They would have walked fully upright (as the name, 'erect man', suggests), and were slightly taller, on average, than modern human beings, with only a slightly smaller brain capacity.

Homo erectus was a stunningly successful species, moving out of Africa to colonize Europe and Asia over the course of its 1.3 million year history. While it is unclear whether *erectus* could speak, it certainly was capable of using fire, and it created elegant hand-axes of the type known as Acheulean tools. Then, several hundred thousand years ago, it faded away, leaving its legacy – the primate known as *Homo sapiens*.

TOP LEFT Homo erectus *skull of Peking Man, the direct ancestor of modern man.*

LEFT *Reconstruction of Peking Man from fossil evidence.*

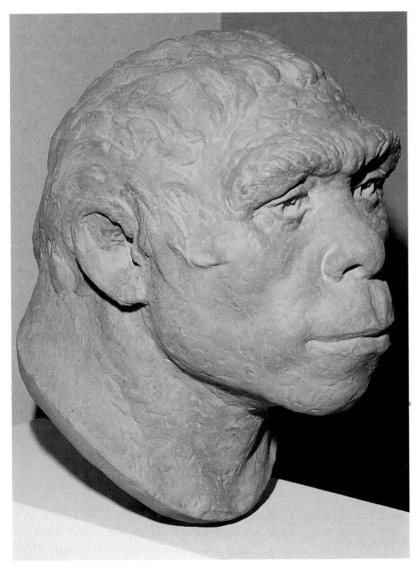

TRACE FOSSILS

Not true fossils in the strictest sense, trace fossils record biological activity without preserving the animal itself. In this category are found fossil worm tubes, mollusc borings and insect tracks, as well as such non-biological pseudo-fossils as 'fossil lightning'.

BIOLOGICAL TRACE FOSSILS

Many trace fossils must remain anonymous, but sometimes the palaeontologist can determine what species made the trace by comparing it to markings found in association with animal fossils or living species; very often, particular genera leave recognizable trails or burrows. These mollusc holes in chalk, for instance, were made by *Pholas* razor clams or *Ensis* angel-wings. Both bivalves are common in the fossil record from the Cretaceous, and remain abundant in today's oceans.

Trace fossils are especially important in deciphering the lives of extinct animals. By measuring the stride lengths of dinosaur footprints, palaeontologists have surmised everything from herd social structure to posture and speed.

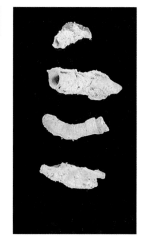

ABOVE *Fossilized worm tubes.*

RIGHT *Volcanic Fulgurites, formed when lightning struck a field of volcanic pumice.*

BELOW *Bore holes made by either* Pholas *or* Ensis *spp.*

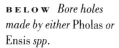

Worm tubes and mollusc borings

PLEISTOCENE

Many species of aquatic worms secrete cement-like substances to bond the substrata into a hard tube; since the tubes were buried in mud to start with, they are frequently found in fossilized form. The worms themselves, on the other hand, are rarely found – the usual fate of soft-bodied animals, which are fossilized only under the most remarkable of conditions.

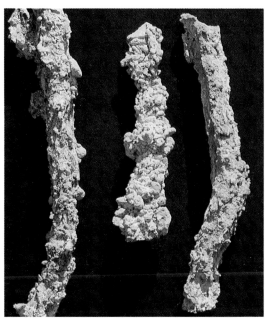

NON-BIOLOGICAL TRACE FOSSILS

Sometimes, the same forces that create a fossil from a dead organism do the same for non-biological phenomena. While not truly fossils, they are often found by fossil hunters, and are fascinating in their own right.

The illustration above shows volcanic fulgurites, formed when lightning struck a field of volcanic pumice, melting and solidifying the mineral into thin, glassy tubes covered with rough pumice.

Glossary

Allochthonus A fossil displaced from or deposited outside its habitat.

Ancestrula Early stage in bryozoan life cycle.

Angiosperms Flowering plants.

Anterior Having to do with the front; in bivalves, the beak points towards the anterior side.

Anthropoids Human-like primates.

Aperture Opening in shell, especially in gastropods and cephalopods.

Apical whorls In gastropods, the whorls comprising the apex or spire.

Aristotle's lantern Five plates that comprise echinoid 'jaw'.

Australopithecine Primitive hominids of the genus *Australopithecus*.

Autochthonous A fossil deposited within its habitat.

Biserial In graptolites, when thecae are found on both sides of the stipe.

Body whorl In gastropods, the largest whorl, containing the majority of the animal's body and ending in the aperture.

BP Before Present.

Brachial valve Upper valve in brachiopods.

Calcareous Containing or consisting of calcium carbonate.

Calice Central 'cup' in corals.

Calyx Budlike body segment of crinoid and similar echinoderms.

Carapace The shieldlike exoskeleton that covers the head and thorax of crustaceans.

Cephalon Trilobite head shield.

Chitinous Consisting of chitin, the horny plating that forms the exoskeleton of arthropods.

Cirri Prehensile armlets on crinoid stems.

Clastic Sedimentary rock composed of rock, mineral or fossil fragments.

Corallite Calcereous exoskeleton of an individual coral animal.

Corallum A coral colony, made up of many corallites.

Costae Radial ribbing on mollusc shells.

Counterpart Imprint or impression left in rock by a fossil.

Equivalve In bivalves, when both valves are the same size and general shape.

Evolute In cephalopods, a type of coiling in which the loose outer coils do not greatly over-lap the inner coils.

Growth lines Radial marks on mollusc and other shells that record shell growth.

Gondwanaland Southern supercontinent comprising South America, Antarctica, Africa and Australia.

Gymnosperms Non-flowering plants, including conifers, cycads and seed-ferns.

Igneous Rock formed from crystallized magma or lava.

Inequivalve In bivalves, when the valves are of differing size and shape.

Internal mould Fossil created when a mineral fills the internal gaps in an organism, which later dissolves.

Involute In cephalopods, a type of coiling in which the tight outer coils overlap the inner coils.

K-T Boundary Division between Cretaceous and Tertiary, marked by mass extinction.

Lanceolate Shaped like a lance, narrowly tapered at both ends.

Laurasia Northern supercontinent composed of Europe and North America.

Matrix Rock surrounding a fossil.

Medusa Free-swimming, saucer-shaped body form rimmed with tentacles, especially jellyfish.

Metamorphic Rock that has undergone change due to heat or pressure.

Mould Gap in matrix left when a fossilized organism completely dissolves.

Natural cast A pseudomorph; the resulting fossil formed when a substance fills an empty mould.

Nonclastic Sedimentary rock formed by the deposition of

animal or plant matter or minerals.

Ossicle Crinoid stem segment.

Palaeontology The study of fossils and the extinct life forms that they represent.

Pangea Supercontinent formed by juncture of Gondwana-land and Laurasia.

Part The fossil itself; opposite of counterpart.

Pedicle foramen Opening for stalk in pedicle valve of brachiopods.

Pedicle valve Lower valve in brachiopods.

Peristome Oral opening in echinoids.

Permineralization Partial mineralization of a fossil.

Pinnules Armlets on crinoid branches used for food gathering.

Pleurae Trilobite 'ribs'.

Polyp Sedentary, columnar body form topped with tentacles, especially of cnidarians.

Posterior Having to do with the rear.

Prosimians Primitive primates, including lemurs.

Pseudomorph Process by which a fossilized organism completely dissolves, leaving a gap in the matrix which is filled by another substance, creating an external mould of the specimen.

Pteridophyte A true fern.

Pteridosperm A seed-fern.

Pygidium Trilobite tail section.

Replacement Complete mineralization of a fossil in which the original substance is replaced by an invading mineral like silica.

Rhabdosome Graptolite colony.

Sedimentary Type of rock formed from layers of deposited sediment.

Septa Dividing wall between chambers in a cephalopod shell.

Septae Lateral dividers inside a corallite.

Sessile Stationary or attached.

Siphuncle Thin tube that joins the flotation chambers in cephalopod shells.

Shoulder In gastropods, the flattened portion of the whorl just below the suture.

Siliceous Containing or consisting of silica.

Siphonal canal In gastropods, a tubelike extension of the aperture.

sp. Abbreviation for species (singular).

spp. Abbreviation for species (plural).

Spatulate Having a broad end and a narrow, tapered base.

Spicules Mineralized structures found in sponge tissue.

Spire All whorls in a gastropod shell except for the body whorl.

Steinkern Internal mould.

Suture Line of juncture between two body parts. In gastropods; the seam between two whorls; in cephalopods, the intricate divisions between the shell wall and septa.

Tabulae Horizontal dividers inside a corallite.

Test The hardened outer shell; especially of *Foraminifera* and some echinoderms.

Theca Calyx, or cup, of crinoid and similar echinoderms.

Thecae Tube on graptolite stipe that encased the living animal.

Thorax Middle of three body sections among arthropods.

Tubercules Knobs, especially on echinoderm tests.

Umbo Curved posterior beak in bivalve shells (plural: umbones).

Uniserial In graptolites, when thecae are found on one side of the stipe only.

Valve Half of a bivalve mollusc or brachiopod shell.

Venter Having to do with the lower, or ventral, side. In ammonoids, it refers to the portion of the whorl farthest from the central axis of the shell.

Whorls Coils, especially of shells.

Zooecia Individual bryozoan animal.

Index

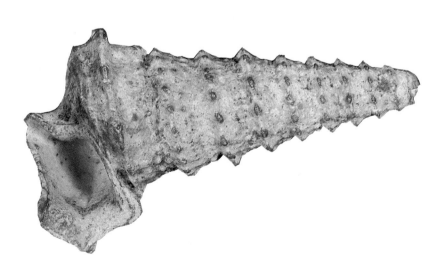

Acknowledgements

Photographs were supplied by the following:

Heather Angel: pp10r, 34t, 50r, 51tl.

Derek Bromhall/Oxford Scientific Films: p30l.

British Museum/Natural History Museum: pp18,
66c, 66tr, 67bl, 68, 69, 70.

C M Dixon: pp6, 7t, 9t, 9b, 17t, 25tr, 29tr, 63tl, 63bl, 66t, 71t, 74t, 74b.

Geoscience Features Picture Library: pp8t, 8b, 10l, 11t, 11b, 12, 13, 14,
16, 17b, 19, 20, 24b, 26, 27, 28, 29tl, 29b, 30, 31, 32, 33, 35, 36, 37, 38, 39, 40,
41, 42, 43, 44, 45, 46, 47, 48, 49, 50l, 51bl, 52, 53, 54, 55, 56, 57, 58, 59, 60,
61, 62, 63r, 64tl, 65, 75.

W J Kennedy/Oxford Scientific Films: p23.

Breck P Kent/Oxford Scientific Films: pp7b, 51tr.

Charles Palek/Earth Scenes/Oxford Scientific Films: p64br;
Charles Palek/Animals Animals/Oxford Scientific Films: p.72.

Sinclair Stammers/Oxford Scientific Films: p52r.

Harry Taylor/Oxford Scientific Films: p34b.

Scott Weidensaul: p24t.

l = left; r = right; t = top; b = bottom